CAPE COD SEASHORE LIFE

SCRIMSHAW PRESS BOOKS BY PAUL GIAMBARBA

Cape Cod Seashore Life
Cape Cod & Cape Cod National Seashore
Whales, Whaling and Whalecraft
Surfmen and Lifesavers
Early Explorers of America
Going Whaling with Cap'n Goody
Around Cape Cod with Cap'n Goody

CAPE COD SEASHORE LIFE

BY PAUL GIAMBARBA

THE SCRIMSHAW PRESS

Distributed by BARRE PUBLISHERS,
Barre, Massachusetts 01005

1968

ACKNOWLEDGEMENT

¶ The author makes grateful acknowledgement for the assistance of Marshal T. Case, Curator, Cape Cod Museum of Natural History, Brewster, for his generous help and careful checking of countless details; and to Agnes McCarthy for her helpful suggestions and comprehensive editing of the manuscript.

Second Printing

Library of Congress Catalog Card Number: 66-19826

Printed in the United States of America

CONTENTS

This helpful book describes and illustrates in a simple, direct way almost 200 plants, reptiles, mammals, birds, fish, insects, mollusks and crustaceans that can be found along the Cape Cod shore.

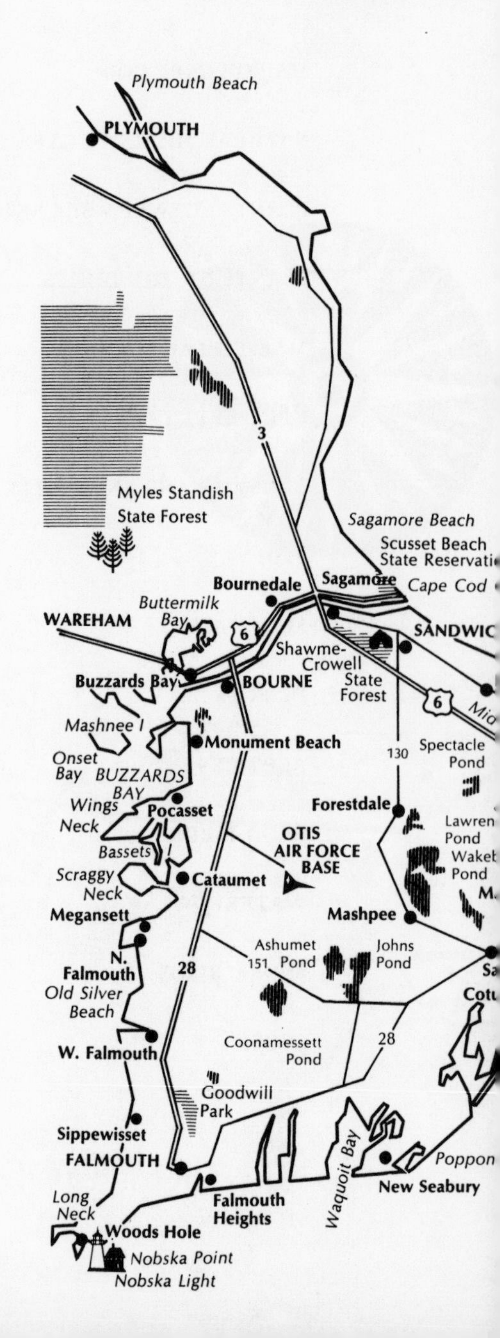

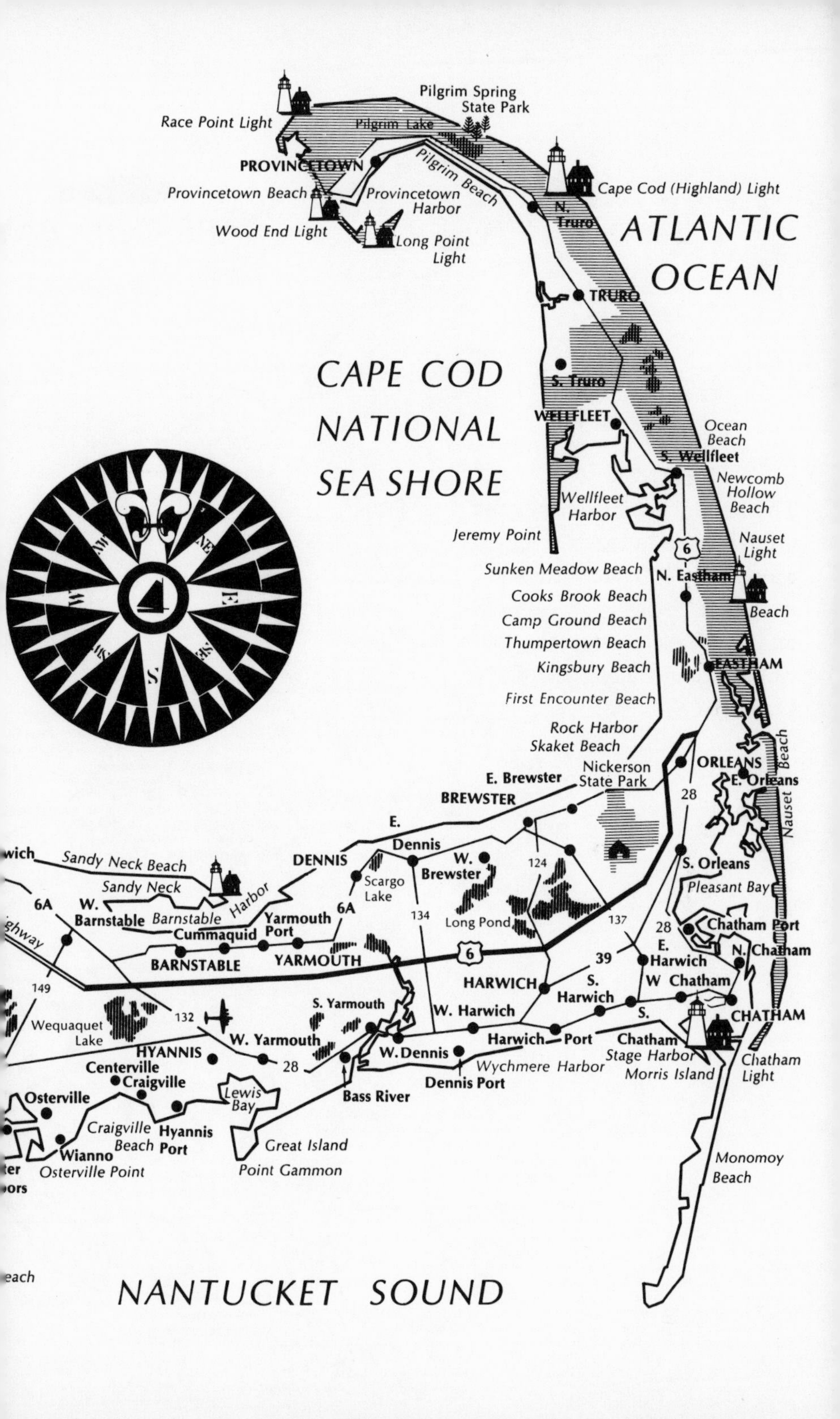

Pilgrim Spring
State Park
Race Point Light
Pilgrim Lake
PROVINCETOWN
Pilgrim Beach
Provincetown Beach
Provincetown
Harbor
Cape Cod (Highland) Light
Wood End Light
Long Point
Light
N.
Truro
ATLANTIC
OCEAN
TRURO
CAPE COD
NATIONAL
SEA SHORE
S. Truro
WELLFLEET
Ocean
Beach
S. Wellfleet
Newcomb
Hollow
Beach
Wellfleet
Harbor
Jeremy Point
Nauset
Light
6
Sunken Meadow Beach
N. Eastham
Cooks Brook Beach
Beach
Camp Ground Beach
Thumpertown Beach
Kingsbury Beach
EASTHAM
First Encounter Beach
Rock Harbor
Skaket Beach
Nauset Beach
Nickerson
State Park
ORLEANS
E. Brewster
E. Orleans
BREWSTER
28
E.
Dennis
124
S. Orleans
Sandy Neck Beach
DENNIS
W.
Brewster
Sandy Neck
Harbor
Scargo
Lake
Pleasant Bay
6A
W.
Barnstable
Barnstable
Yarmouth
Port
6A
134
Long Pond
137
28
Chatham Port
Cummaquid
E.
N. Chatham
6
39
Harwich
BARNSTABLE
YARMOUTH
HARWICH
S.
Harwich
W Chatham
149
S. Yarmouth
W. Harwich
S.
CHATHAM
132
Wequaquet
Lake
W. Yarmouth
Harwich Port
Chatham
HYANNIS
W. Dennis
Stage Harbor
Chatham
Light
28
Wychmere Harbor
Centerville
Craigville
Morris Island
Dennis Port
Lewis
Bay
Bass River
Osterville
Craigville
Beach
Hyannis
Port
Great Island
Wianno
Monomoy
Beach
Osterville Point
Point Gammon
NANTUCKET SOUND

CAPE COD SEASHORE LIFE

NATURAL HISTORY

For thousands of years, the Atlantic has been battering these sandy shores, shaping and reshaping the coastline. Northeast gales have persistently scooped out beaches and shifted sand dunes. Days of brilliant sunshine are followed by rolling fogs and thin mists, and a quiet sea can become an ogre overnight. One is quickly impressed by the vastness and strength of nature along the Cape shoreline. It is the "wonder-strand" of the Viking explorers—a place where, Thoreau said, ". . . a man may stand and put all America behind him."

And living in this big shore-world are countless millions of forms of life, some large, some too small for the eye to see, many delicate beyond our imagining. They have survived the centuries and thrived as well.

The following pages describe and illustrate many of the plants and animals a careful searcher may come upon within the confines of Cape Cod.

Bordering the sea and back of the tidal flats are the salt marshes. There, microscopic vegetable organisms abound and tiny marine animals are hatched. The movement of the tides carries this rich food material over a sweeping area of the sea, where it is eaten by fish, shellfish, and crustaceans.

It takes thousands of years for a marsh to form and for the intricate pattern of vegetable and animal life to develop. Once a marsh is destroyed, it can never be restored. Where tidal marshes have been dredged and filled, ocean and shellfish have disappeared, along with the seabirds that feed on them.

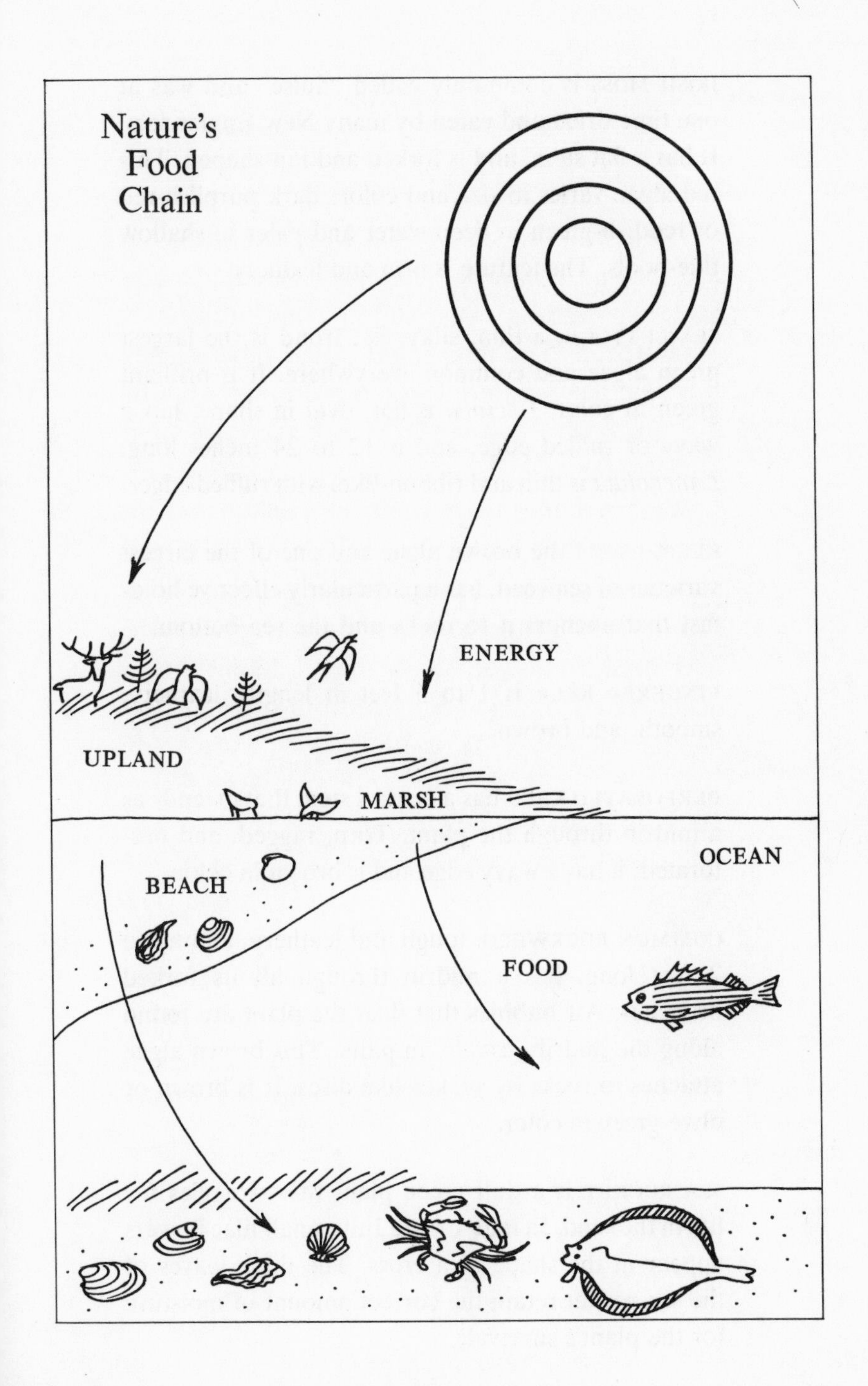
Nature's
Food
Chain
ENERGY
UPLAND
MARSH
OCEAN
BEACH
FOOD

IRISH MOSS is commonly called "dulse" and was at one time dried and eaten by many New Englanders. It has a flat stem, and is forked and fan-shaped. This red algae varies in size and color: dark purplish-red or reddish-green in deep water and paler in shallow tide-pools. The texture is firm and leathery.

SEA LETTUCE, a thin, silky, flat frond is the largest green algae and common everywhere. It is brilliant green in color. *Lactuca* is flat, oval in shape, has a wavy or ruffled edge, and is 12 to 24 inches long. *Lanceolata* is thin and ribbon-like, with ruffled edges.

KELP, one of the brown algae and one of the largest varieties of seaweed, has a particularly effective hold-fast that anchors it to rocks and the sea-bottom.

FINGERED KELP is 1 to 5 feet in length, leathery, smooth, and brown.

PERFORATED KELP has a central stem that extends as a midrib through the plant. Torn, ragged, and perforated, it has a wavy edge and is brown in color.

COMMON ROCKWEED, tough and leathery, and up to 2 feet long, has a midrib through all its forked branches. Air bubbles that float the plant are found along the midrib, usually in pairs. This brown algae attaches to rocks by sucker-like discs. It is brown or olive-green in color.

SEA ROCKET is a dull green plant that struggles for life in the sand. In mid- or late July, small lilac flowers appear in the shape of a cross. The thick leaves of the sea rocket retain the correct amount of moisture for the plant's survival.

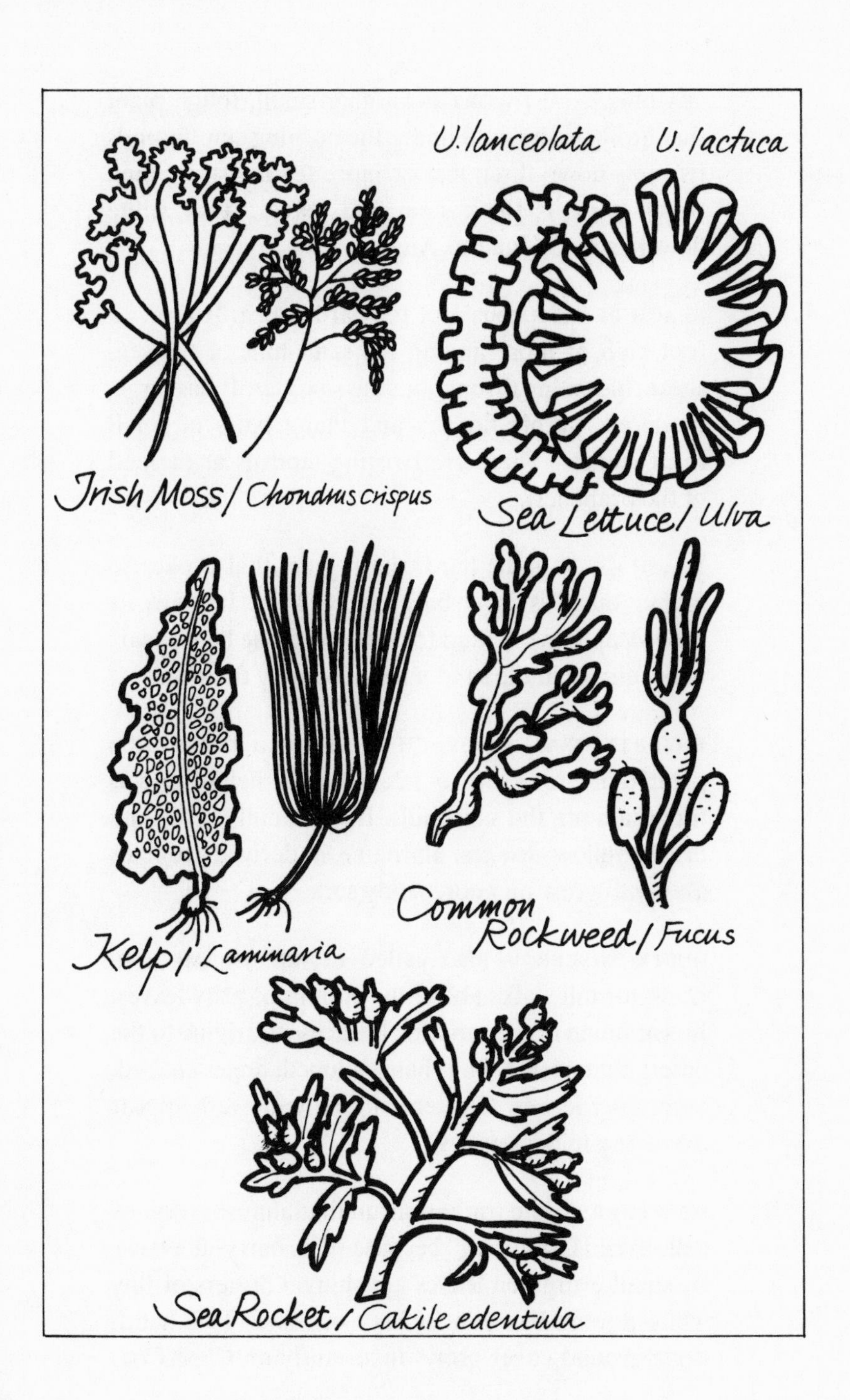
U. lanceolata
U. lactuca
Irish Moss / Chondrus crispus
Sea Lettuce / Ulva
Kelp / Laminaria
Common Rockweed / Fucus
Sea Rocket / Cakile edentula

SEA BEACH SANDWORT is another small, tough plant that grows in the sand under the burning sun. It sends its roots down three feet or more for moisture, then stores it in its thick stem and leaves. Tiny white flowers appear June to August.

BEACH PEA is a cousin of the garden pea. It grows a foot high or more among the sand hills of the seashore, blooming throughout the summer. It has large, clustered, purple flowers and many pairs of small thick leaflets. There are twisting tendrils at the end of the branches.

BEACH GRASS is the hard, sharp grass that evokes so many "ouch"es from barefoot walkers. It sends its roots deep into the sand for moisture. The bent spears make circles in the sand when blown by the wind.

POVERTY GRASS or BEACH HEATH is a bushy little plant that grows up to 12 inches in height and is found among the sand hills. It has small leaves and bright yellow flowers. Its name is derived from its ability to grow on poor, sandy soil.

DUSTY MILLER is also called BEACH WORMWOOD. Look for tall stalks above the clumps of ashy leaves. It is at home in the sand for it traces its origins to the desert regions of Asia. It has scalloped, finger-shaped, furry gray leaves. Clusters of yellow flowers appear from July to September.

BEARBERRY is the trailing shrub that almost everyone calls "Wild Cranberry" because of its berry-like fruit. Its small evergreen leaves are shiny. Clusters of tiny white flowers blossom in May or June. This handsome ground cover grows luxuriantly on Cape Cod.

Sea Beach Sandwort
Arenaria peploides
Beach Pea
Lathyrus maritimus
Beach Grass
Ammophila breviligulata
Poverty Grass or Beach Heath
Hudsonia tomentosa
Dusty Miller
Artemisia stelleriana
Bearberry
Arctostaphylos Uva-ursi

BAYBERRY is a compact, many-branched shrub from 2 to 8 feet in height. It has smooth, shiny, fragrant leaves about 1 to 3 inches long. The little gray berries are boiled in water and the wax is skimmed off to make bayberry candles. These are very aromatic, less greasy than ordinary candles, and smokeless after snuffing.

BEACH PLUM, a straggling bush with many branches, grows 2 to 5 feet in height. White flowers appear in April and May. The fruit is ½ to 1 inch in diameter and purple or crimson in color. The bark of the shrub is quite dark, and the leaves have a fine-toothed edge. Beach Plums are picked in August for preserving.

SALT SPRAY ROSE is a wild rose which perfumes the summer air wherever it grows. Fragrant, purplish, pink, and white flowers adorn this hardy seaside plant. The leaves are dark green and serrated. Behind the wilted blossoms are the red rose hips, or fruit, rich in vitamin C from their long exposure to the sun.

BEAR OAK is called that because bears were particularly fond of its acorns. This is a small shrub from 3 to 8 feet in height with many branches. The leaves are 2 to 4 inches long and usually have 5 lobes. The acorns are almost ½ inch in length. There are no bears on Cape Cod.

PITCH PINE has needles, 3 to 6 inches long, in bunches of three. The tree is a hard wood full of pitch and has a thick, dark, rough bark. The cones have curved, pointed scales , and are 2 to 3 inches in length.

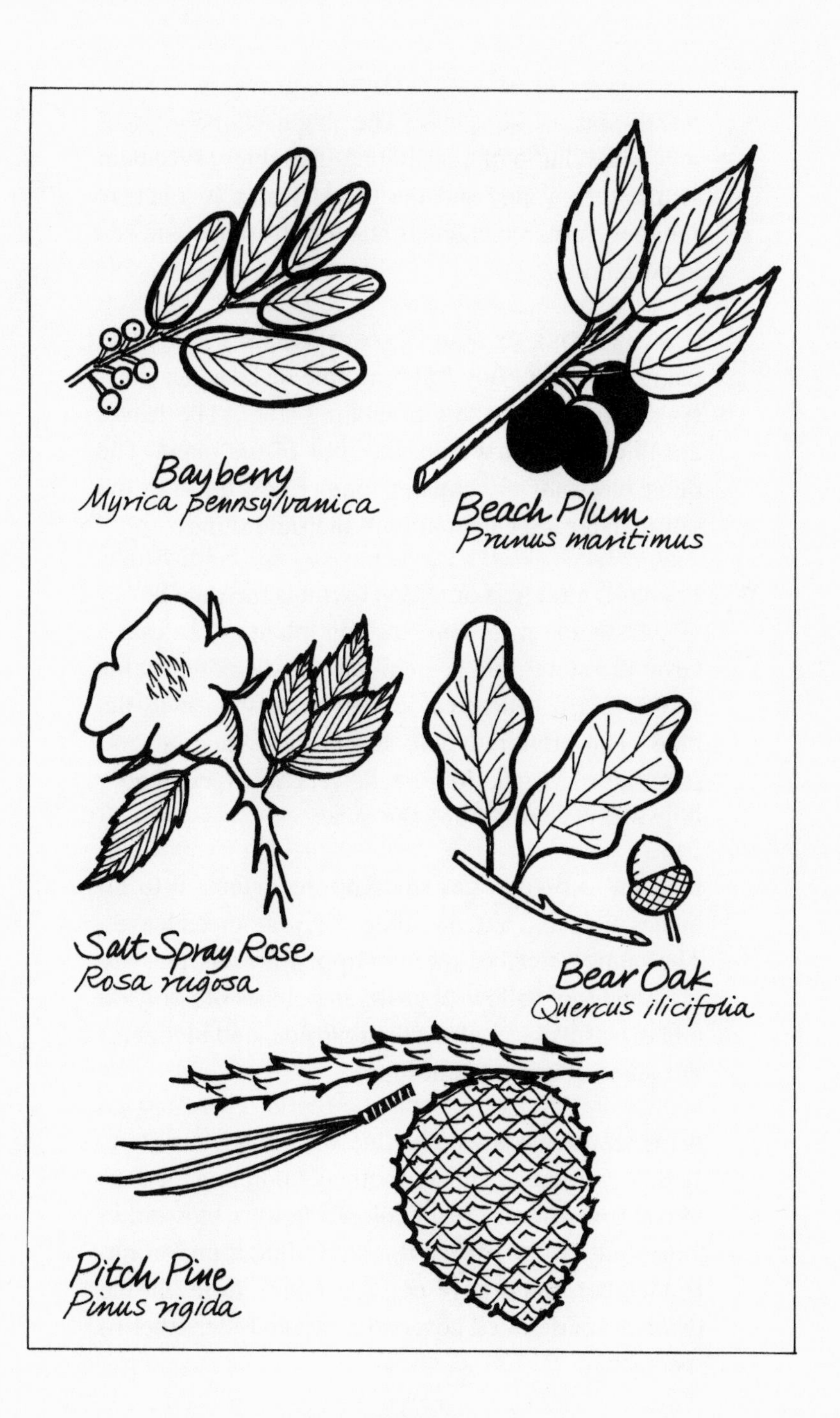
Bayberry
Myrica pennsylvanica
Beach Plum
Prunus maritimus
Salt Spray Rose
Rosa rugosa
Bear Oak
Quercus ilicifolia
Pitch Pine
Pinus rigida

GLASSWORT or MARSH SAMPHIRE grows in the salt marsh and in the dunes. The shape of the plant is much like that of a candelabra. The thick, succulent stems store water, and the plant, which is green in summer, turns spectacular shades of orange and red in autumn.

SEA LAVENDER or MARSH ROSEMARY is a spray-like plant with many tiny fragrant blue or lavender flowers on a single leafless branching stem. The leaves are thick and grow from the root of the plant. The plant blossoms all summer long. Look for it in the salt marsh rather than among the sand dunes.

TRAILING ARBUTUS or MAYFLOWER is the state flower of Massachusetts. This trailing plant, also called Ground Laurel, has a stem with rust-colored hairs, and rounded evergreen leaves, heart-shaped at the base. The clustered pink flowers are fragrant and star-shaped. Look for mayflowers in April, under fallen leaves and among the pines.

BUTTER-AND-EGGS has smooth, erect stems 6 to 30 inches high, and narrow, alternate, gray-green leaves. The name describes the two-tipped flowers that are two shades of yellow. It grows in patches of poor soil and in waste places along the roadside, and blooms in late summer and early autumn.

BITTERSWEET is a woody vine with a twisting stem. It has alternate, finely-toothed, pointing leaves. Small, greenish or cream-colored flowers blossom in June, but it is the fruit of this shrub that is important. In October, the orange pods curl back to reveal the brilliant scarlet seed covers that make bittersweet so spectacular.

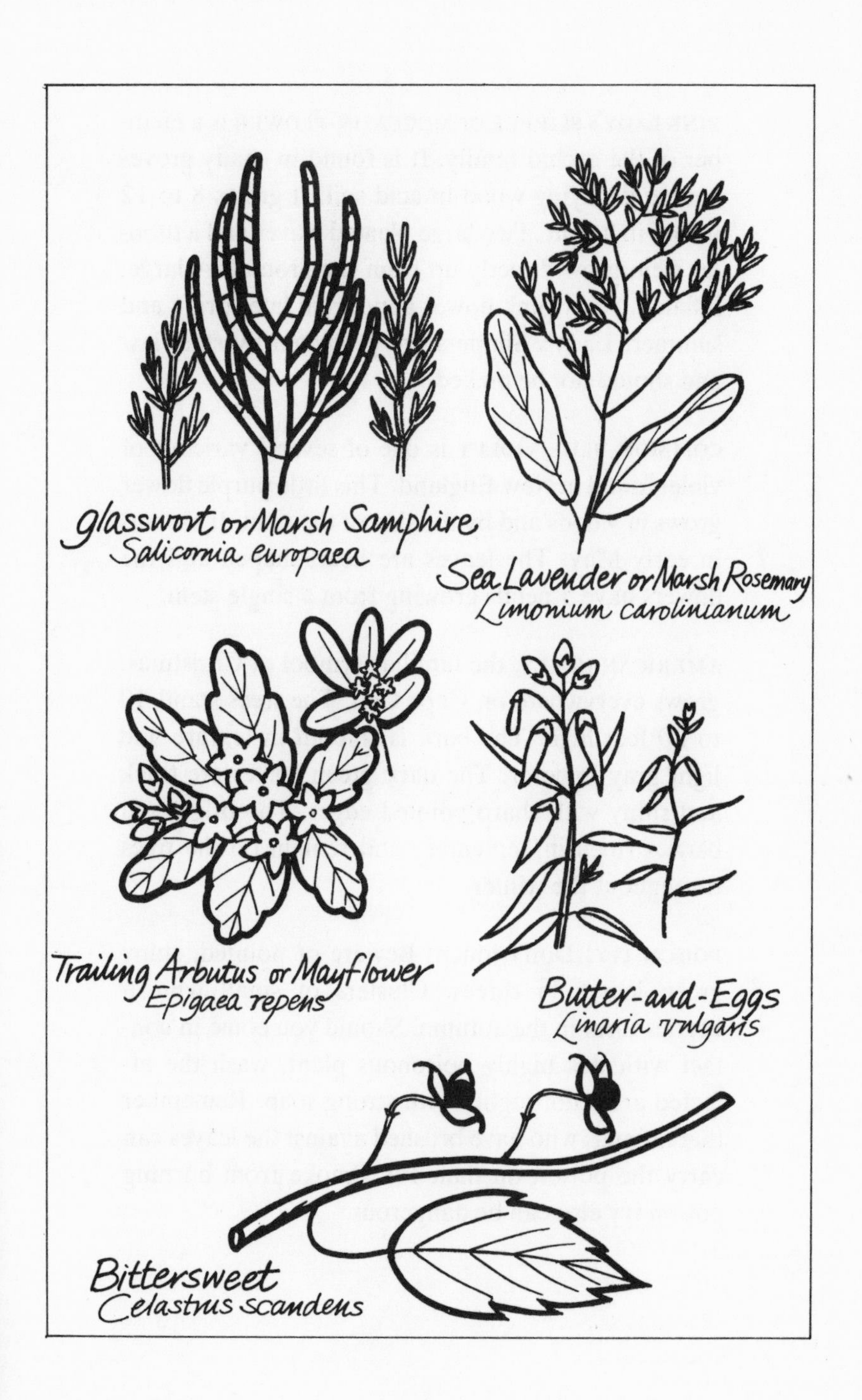

Glasswort or Marsh Samphire
Salicornia europaea
Sea Lavender or Marsh Rosemary
Limonium carolinianum
Trailing Arbutus or Mayflower
Epigaea repens
Butter-and-Eggs
Linaria vulgaris
Bittersweet
Celastrus scandens

PINK LADY'S SLIPPER or MOCCASIN-FLOWER is a member of the orchid family. It is found in shady groves among decaying wood in acid soil. It grows 8 to 12 inches in height .Two large pleated leaves and a tubular stem grow directly up from the ground. A large, inflated, veiny pink flower appears in late spring and summer. Lady's Slippers are protected by state law and should not be picked.

COMMON BLUE VIOLET is one of several varieties of violet found in New England. This little purple flower grows in woods and by the side of the road. It blooms in early May. The leaves are heart-shaped and the flowers have 5 petals growing from a single stem.

AMERICAN HOLLY, the familiar symbol of Christmas, grows everywhere on Cape Cod. The trees stand 10 to 30 feet high. The bark is smooth in texture and light gray in color. The dark green leaves are thick and shiny with sharp pointed edges. The bright red berries ripen in September and remain on the trees throughout the winter.

POISON IVY! Don't touch! Beware of pointed, shiny green leaves in threes. Clusters of small whitish berries form in the autumn. Should you come in contact with this highly poisonous plant, wash the affected area thoroughly with strong soap. Remember that animals who have brushed against the leaves can carry the poison on their fur. Smoke from burning poison ivy also can be dangerous.

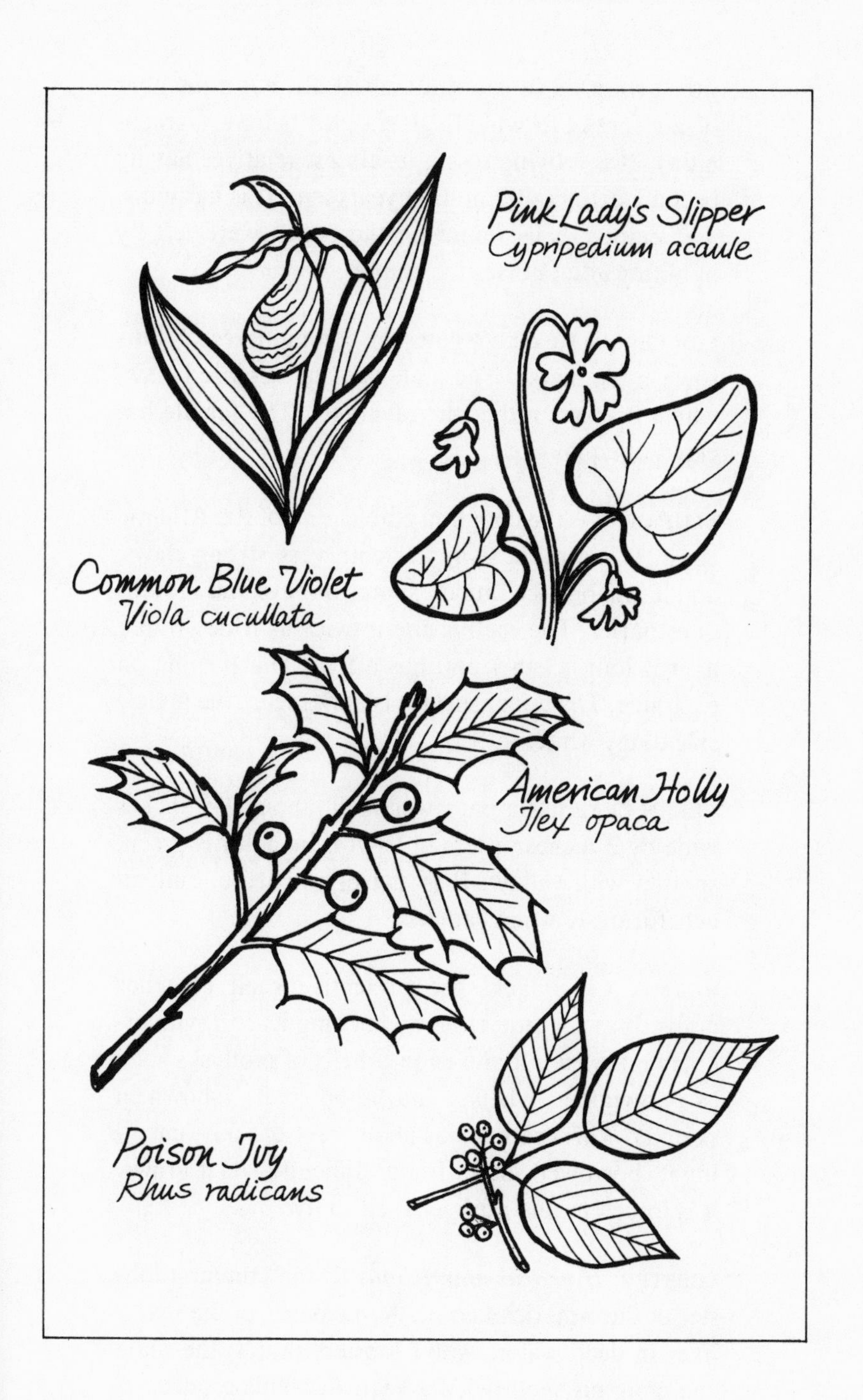
Pink Lady's Slipper
Cypripedium acaule
Common Blue Violet
Viola cucullata
American Holly
Ilex opaca
Poison Ivy
Rhus radicans

HORSESHOE CRAB is not a crab at all, but a member of the family to which spiders also belong (Arachnida). It is a living fossil, its closest relatives having become extinct 400 million years ago. It is harmless. The empty shells found on the beach were left by moulting adult horseshoe crabs.

FIDDLER CRAB congregates in communities of burrows in the marsh. The male has one out-sized claw, which it waves rather threateningly. The female has claws of equal size.

BLUE CRAB is the common edible crab of the Atlantic coast. It is a rapid swimmer with very strong claws, and it inhabits the muddy shores of bays and mouths of estuaries. The shell is about twice as wide (6 in.) as it is long (3 in.) and has a long, sharp spine on each side. The upper surface is dark green, the underside dingy white.

GREEN CRAB has a narrower shell, about 2½ inches wide by 2 inches or less in length. Its color is green, spotted with yellow. It is a lively creature, and reacts furiously when caught.

HERMIT CRAB lacks the protective shell of other crabs. It seeks protection by backing its soft, vulnerable abdomen into the empty shells of mollusks such as periwinkles, whelks, and moon snails (shown in sketch). This crab moves about very quickly, carrying its borrowed shell without difficulty. As it grows, it is forced to find a larger shell to live in.

LOBSTER, *Homarus americanus,* is the common lobster of the American coast. A scavenger of the sea, it lives in deep water. Adult lobsters moult, the male changing his shell twice a year, the female once.

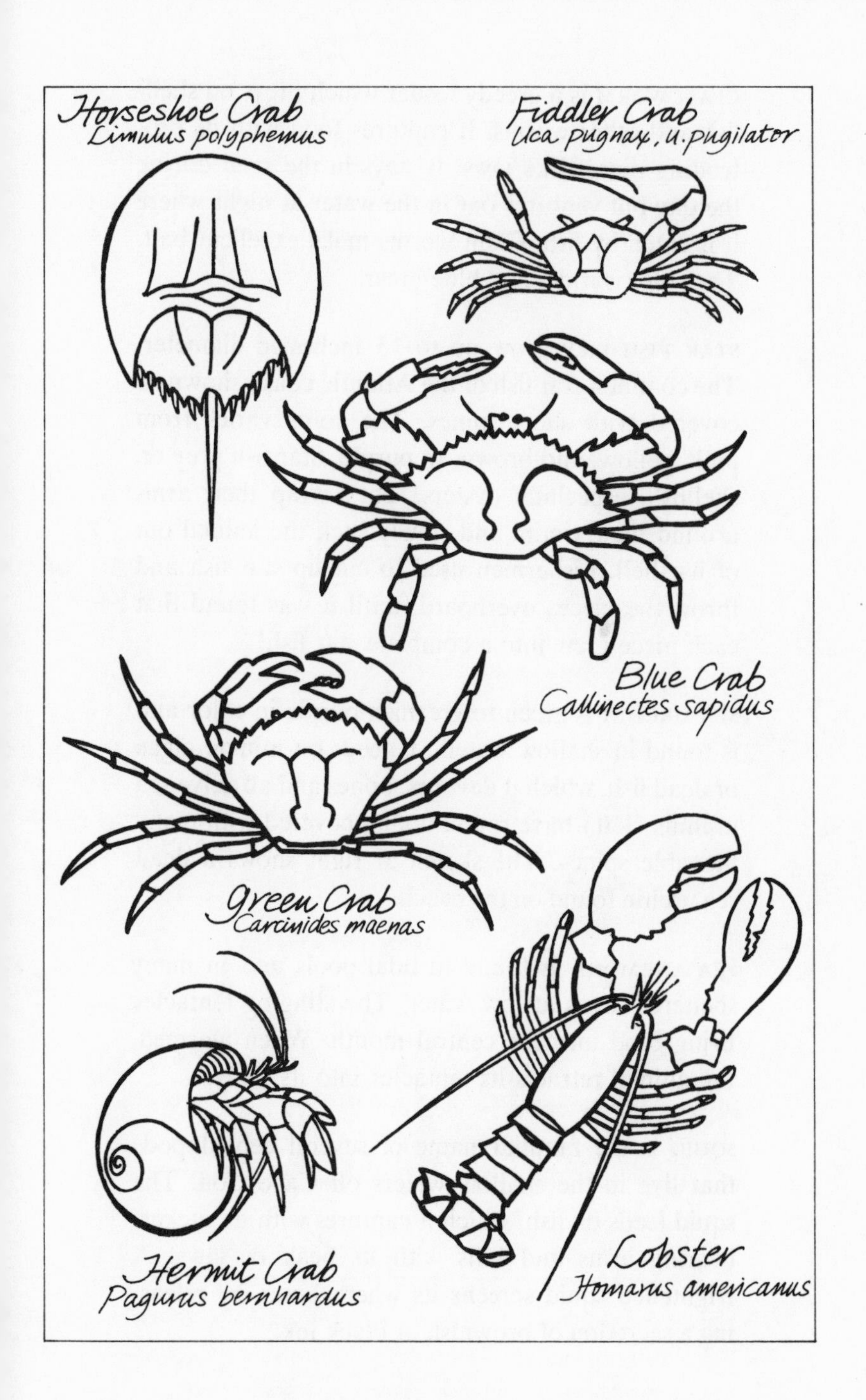
Horseshoe Crab
Limulus polyphemus
Fiddler Crab
Uca pugnax, U. pugilator
Blue Crab
Callinectes sapidus
Green Crab
Carcinides maenas
Hermit Crab
Pagurus bernhardus
Lobster
Homarus americanus

CLAM WORM is a greedy feeder which preys on shellfish and other worms. It captures food with its protruding pincer-like jaws. It stays in the sand during the day but ventures out in the water at night where it is eaten by fish. Clam worms make excellent bait. The color is iridescent blue-green.

STAR FISH may grow up to 15 inches in diameter. The common star fish of the Atlantic coast, shown, is covered with short spines. The color varies from pink, yellow, and brown, to purple. Star fish prey on shellfish, especially oysters. They wrap their arms around their victim and slowly suck the animal out of its shell. Fishermen used to cut up star fish and throw the pieces overboard, until it was found that each piece grew into a complete star fish!

SEA URCHIN is green to greenish-purple in color and is found in shallow waters. It feeds on minute algae or dead fish, which it devours, bones and all. Live sea urchins (left) have round bodies covered with many movable spines. The sketch at right shows a dead sea urchin found on the beach.

SEA ANEMONE is found in tidal pools and in many sheltered areas at low water. The stinging tentacles bring food into the central mouth. When alarmed, the animal retracts its tentacles into its body.

SQUID is the familiar name of several cephalopods that live in the shallow waters off Cape Cod. The squid feeds on fish, which it captures with its sucker-bearing arms and kills with its beak or jaws. A frightened squid screens its whereabouts by releasing a secretion of brownish or black ink.

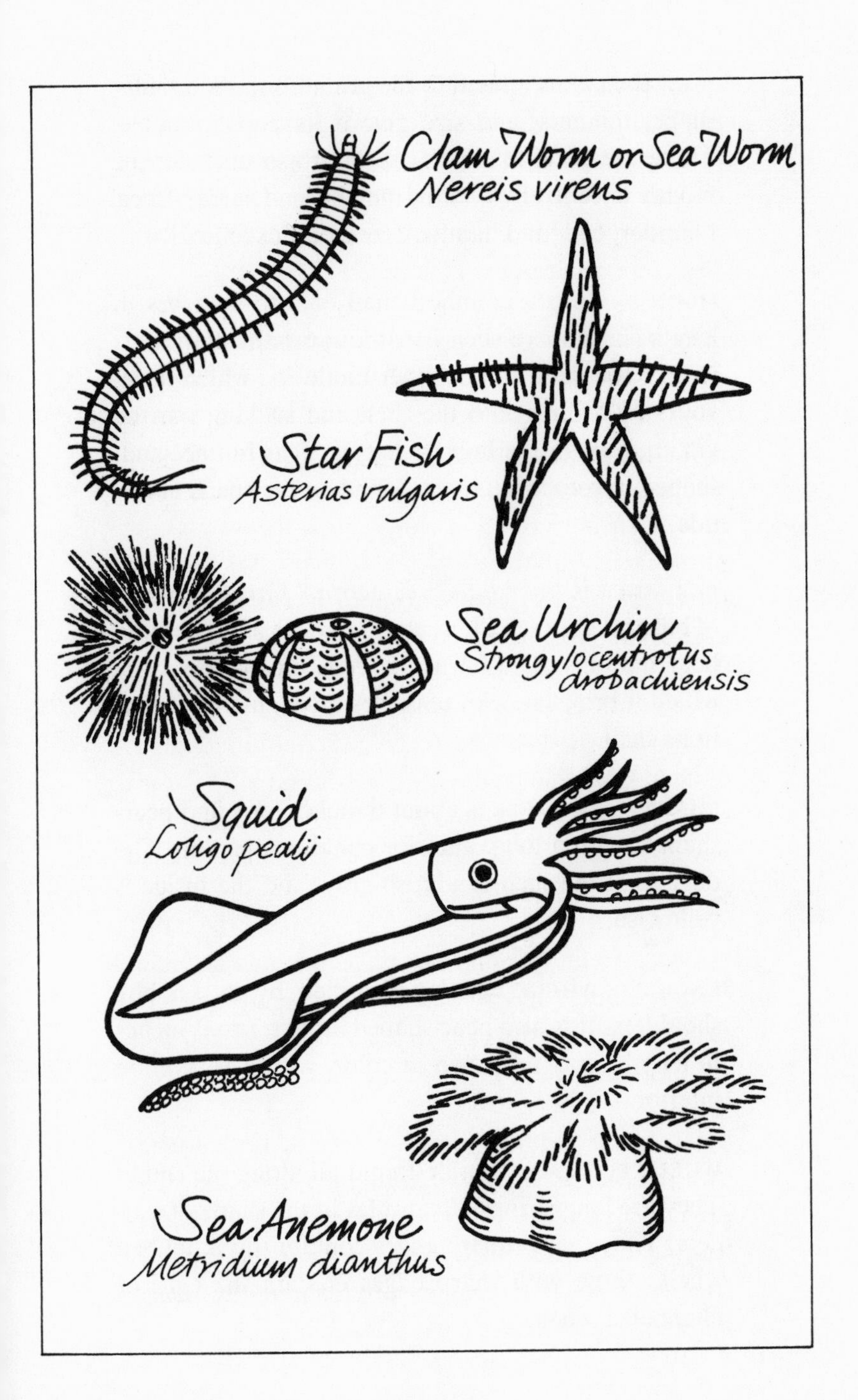
Clam Worm or Sea Worm
Nereis virens
Star Fish
Asterias vulgaris
Sea Urchin
Strongylocentrotus
drobachiensis
Squid
Loligo pealii
Sea Anemone
Metridium dianthus

SAND DOLLAR is related to the sea urchin. Its circular shape, thinness, and size give it its popular name. There are petal-like rays on the upper surface; the mouth is centrally located on the underside. Local flounder, cod, and haddock feed on this animal.

MOON SNAIL is a common snail of 2 to 4 inches in length. Its smooth shell is without ornamentation. It feeds upon dead fish or other mollusks, which it devours by drilling into the shell and sucking out the victim through the hole. It lays its eggs in fine sand, shaped into collars that are found on the beach at low tide.

BARNACLE is known as "sea acorn." Great numbers of barnacles attach themselves to rocks and piles and boat bottoms. The barnacle feeds on minute algae which it brings in with tentacles through a trap door in its shell.

CHANNELED WHELK is about 6 inches long and pear-shaped, with a long, anterior canal or opening. The outside of the shell is whitish-gray, and the inside is yellowish.

KNOBBED WHELK can be identified by its knobby shoulders. It is also pear-shaped, about 7 to 9 inches in length, gray to brown in color, with a vermillion interior.

WHELK EGG CASES can be found all along the shore. They are long strings of capsules in the shape of saucers. Those with square edges contain tiny knobbed whelk; those with sharp edges contain the eggs of channeled whelk.

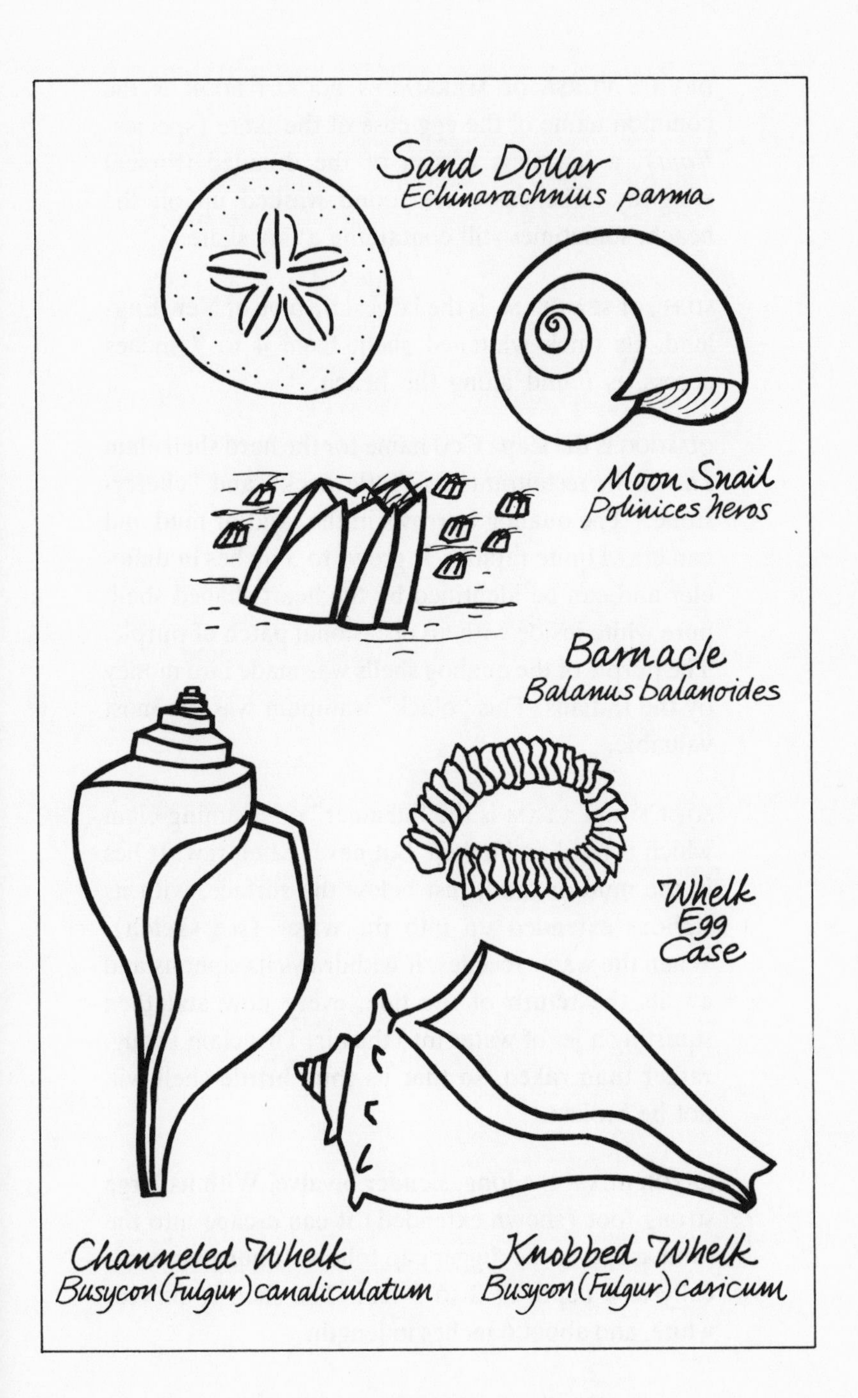
Sand Dollar
Echinarachnius parma
Moon Snail
Polinices heros
Barnacle
Balanus balanoides
Whelk
Egg
Case
Channeled Whelk
Busycon (Fulgur) canaliculatum
Knobbed Whelk
Busycon (Fulgur) caricum

DEVIL'S PURSE or MERMAID'S POCKET-BOOK is the common name of the egg case of the skate (species: *Raja*), a harmless cousin of the dreaded tropical sting-ray. The cases are found washed up on the beach, sometimes still containing a tiny skate.

SURF, or SEA CLAM, is the largest bivalve of New England. Its thick whitened shell, from 4 to 7 inches across, is found along the beach.

QUAHOG is the Cape Cod name for the hard shell clam known in restaurants as "little neck" and "cherrystone." The quahog burrows in the sand or mud and can crawl quite rapidly. It grows to 3 inches in diameter and can be identified by the heart-shaped shell, pure white inside with an occasional patch of purple. The purple of the quahog shells was made into money by the Indians. This "black" wampum was the most valuable.

SOFT SHELL CLAM is the "steamer" or steaming-clam which is fried and baked, but never eaten raw. It lies in the mud or sand, just below the surface, with its siphons extended up into the water (see sketch). When the water recedes, it withdraws its siphons and awaits the return of the tide, every now and then squirting a jet of water into the air. This clam is dug, rather than raked, so that its thin, brittle shell will not be broken.

RAZOR CLAM is a long, slender bivalve. With its large strong foot (shown extended) it can escape into the sand as fast as the digger can follow. It burrows vertically to a depth of 2 to 3 feet. The shell is curved, white, and about 6 inches in length.

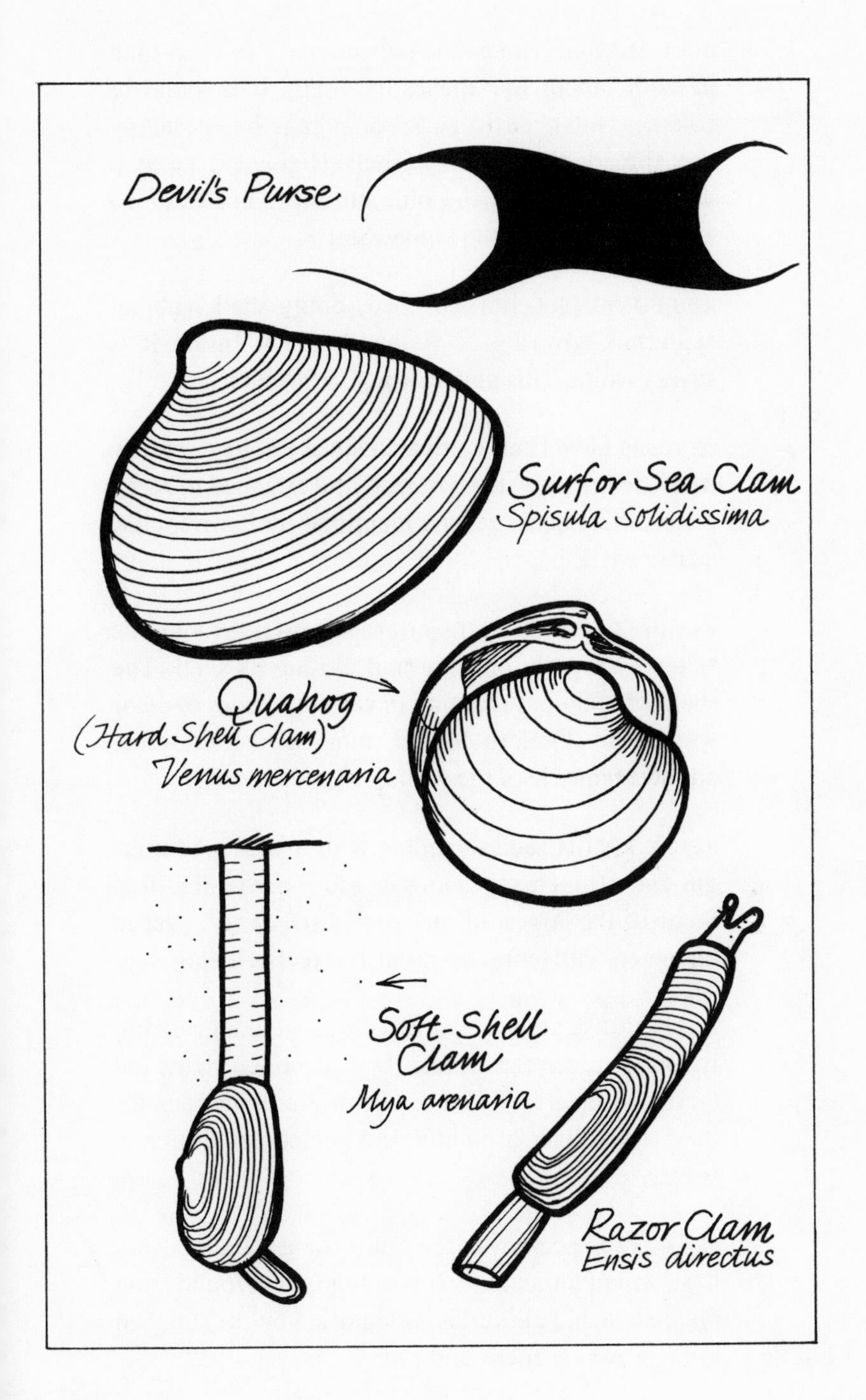
Devil's Purse
Surf or Sea Clam
Spisula solidissima
Quahog
(Hard Shell Clam)
Venus mercenaria
Soft-Shell
Clam
Mya arenaria
Razor Clam
Ensis directus

BLUE MUSSEL is an edible mussel, black or deep-blue in color, about 2½ inches in length. It is found in colonies, attached to rocks or pilings by the many tiny threads that edge the shell. Highly prized as a delicacy in France, the blue mussel is not eaten to any great extent in the United States.

RIBBED MUSSEL has a ribbed, dingy shell with an epidermis covering of yellowish-green. Inside it is silvery white. This mussel is not to be eaten.

OYSTERS have been cultivated since the first century B.C. The uncultivated oyster, found attached to rocks or to other shells, can be identified by its irregular, coarse shell.

BAY OR "CAPE" SCALLOP jet-propels itself through the water by rapidly opening and closing its shell. The shells of scallops are found in varying shades of color with about 20 elevated and rounded ribs. Only the adductor muscle of the scallop is eaten.

JELLY FISH is reddish-yellow with a scalloped margin and 10 inches or more in width across the disc. Some of the largest of the species are up to 8 feet in diameter, with tentacles about 100 feet in length.

PORTUGUESE MAN-O-WAR is a unique animal generally found in warmer waters. It is identified by its red crest and blue sail. The tentacles are dangerous for they can deliver a painful and sometimes disabling sting.

SEA PORK is a colony of sea squirts or ascidians, a very low form of animal life. It is orange when found fresh on the beach, pale yellow when dried by the sun. Sea Pork grows on rocks and pilings.

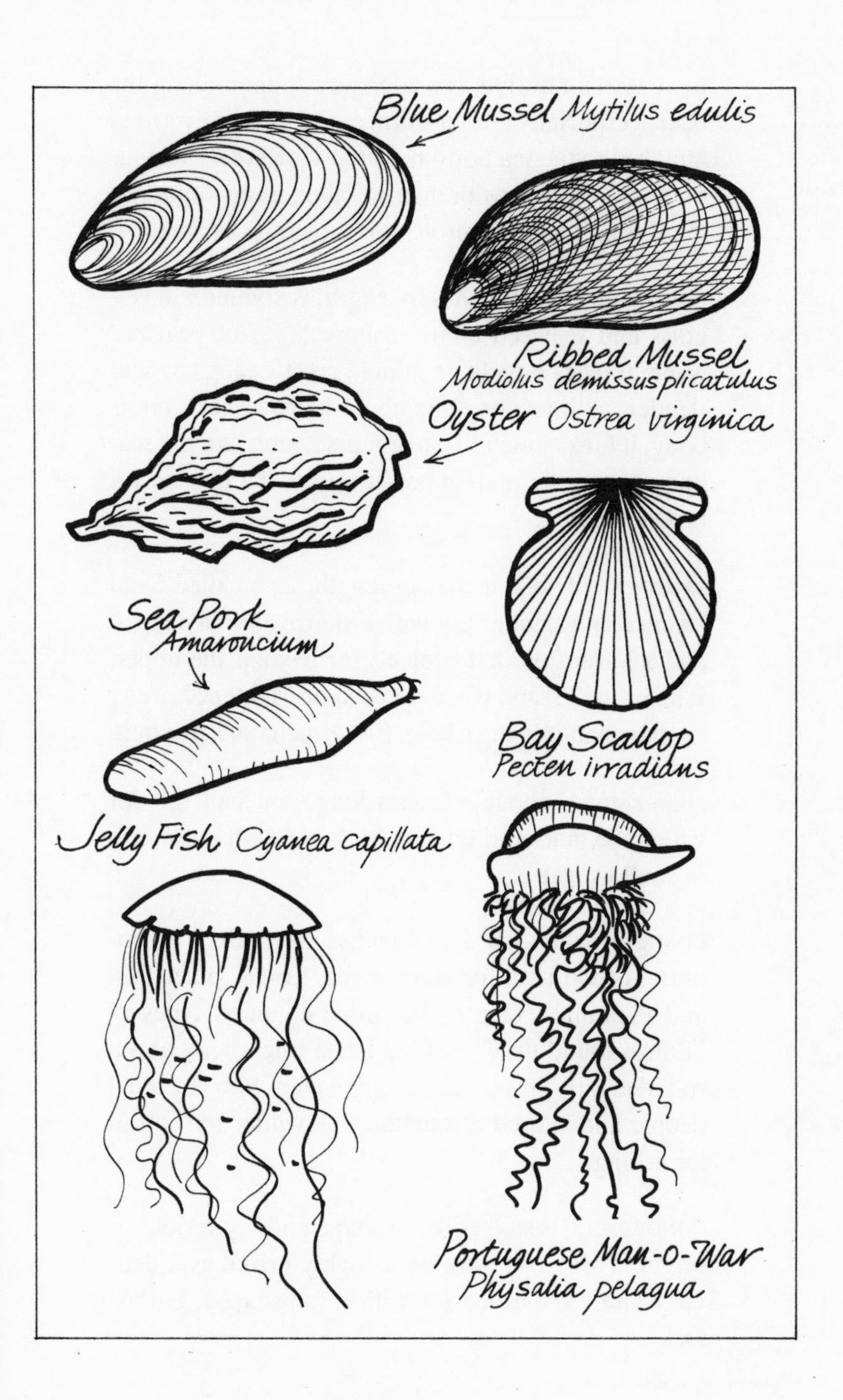
Blue Mussel Mytilus edulis
Ribbed Mussel
Modiolus demissus plicatulus
Oyster Ostrea virginica
Sea Pork
Amaroucium
Bay Scallop
Pecten irradians
Jelly Fish Cyanea capillata
Portuguese Man-o-War
Physalia pelagua

DEADMAN'S FINGERS is a sponge, common along the beach, especially after a storm at sea. It usually grows attached to the sea bottom, but also grows on various bivalves. Yellow to orange in color when found on the shore, it has numerous pores over its surface.

PIPEFISH, 4 to 12 inches in length, is common in eelgrass and seaweed along inshore areas of beaches, where it feeds largely on minute crustacea. Long and slender, with its dorsal fin about halfway back on its body, it looks much like a seahorse; and, like the seahorse male, the male pipefish nurses the eggs in his brood pouch.

SAND EEL, 4 to 6 inches in length, also called Sand Launce, is a slender fish with a sharply pointed snout and a lower jaw that projects far beyond the upper. It hides in the sand when pursued or frightened, using its sharp snout to dig a hole. Fishermen use it for bait.

SILVERSIDES, about 3 inches long, is a bait fish for which the gulls and terns fight. It is found in schools in shallow water.

COMMON KILLIFISH, 2 to 4 inches in length, is an important food item for many birds, turtles, other fish, and mammals. One of the three common types of killifish found on Cape Cod has a thick body and a rounded tail. This is called "salt water chub" by local people and is used throughout the winter for bait in ice fishing.

CONGER EEL is snake-like in shape and mysterious in origin. These eels were once highly prized as a delicacy and were fished for with a fan-shaped, barbed fork.

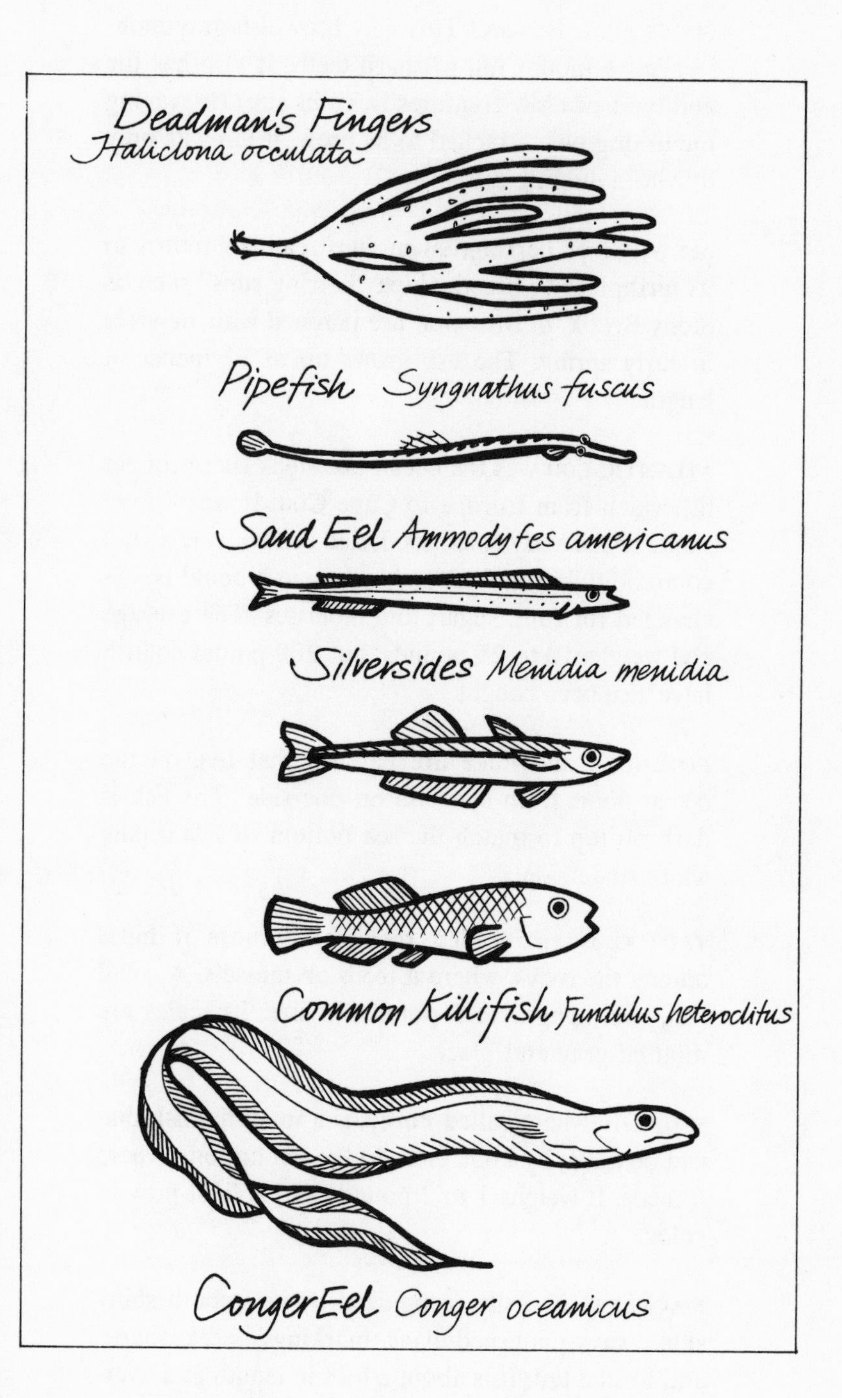
Deadman's Fingers
Haliclona occulata
Pipefish Syngnathus fuscus
Sand Eel Ammodytes americanus
Silversides Menidia menidia
Common Killifish Fundulus heteroclitus
Conger Eel Conger oceanicus

GOOSE FISH: Beware! This ugly brownish-gray monster has a mouth full of sharp teeth. It also has the ability to swallow creatures twice its size. By waving the fishing pole attached to its brow, it lures its prey to within gulping distance.

ALEWIFE, or herring, swims upstream to return to its birthplace to breed. Cape "herring runs" such as Stony Brook, in Brewster, are jammed with alewives in early spring. The fish grows up to 12 inches in length.

ATLANTIC COD was the ocean beefsteak that brought fishermen from Europe to Cape Cod. It was a food staple of the early colonists. Dried cod became a vital commodity in the West Indies, where it could be exchanged for rum, sugar, and molasses. The average cod weighs 10 to 25 pounds, but 200-pound codfish have also been caught.

FLOUNDER and fluke are flat fish that live on the ocean floor. Both eyes are on one side. The fish is dark on top to match the sea bottom. It has a pale white underside.

TAUTOG is also called rockfish, because it hides among the rocks, where it feeds on mussels. A small fish, averaging 2 to 5 pounds in size, its scales are mottled gray and black.

SCUP, elsewhere called Porgy, is a small flat fish that can be taken by hook close to the sea bottom, where it feeds. It weighs 1 to 2 pounds and is light gray in color.

MACKEREL is easily recognized by its smooth shiny skin, wavy-patterned back markings, sleek shape, and forked tail. It is about a foot in length and averages 1½ pounds in weight.

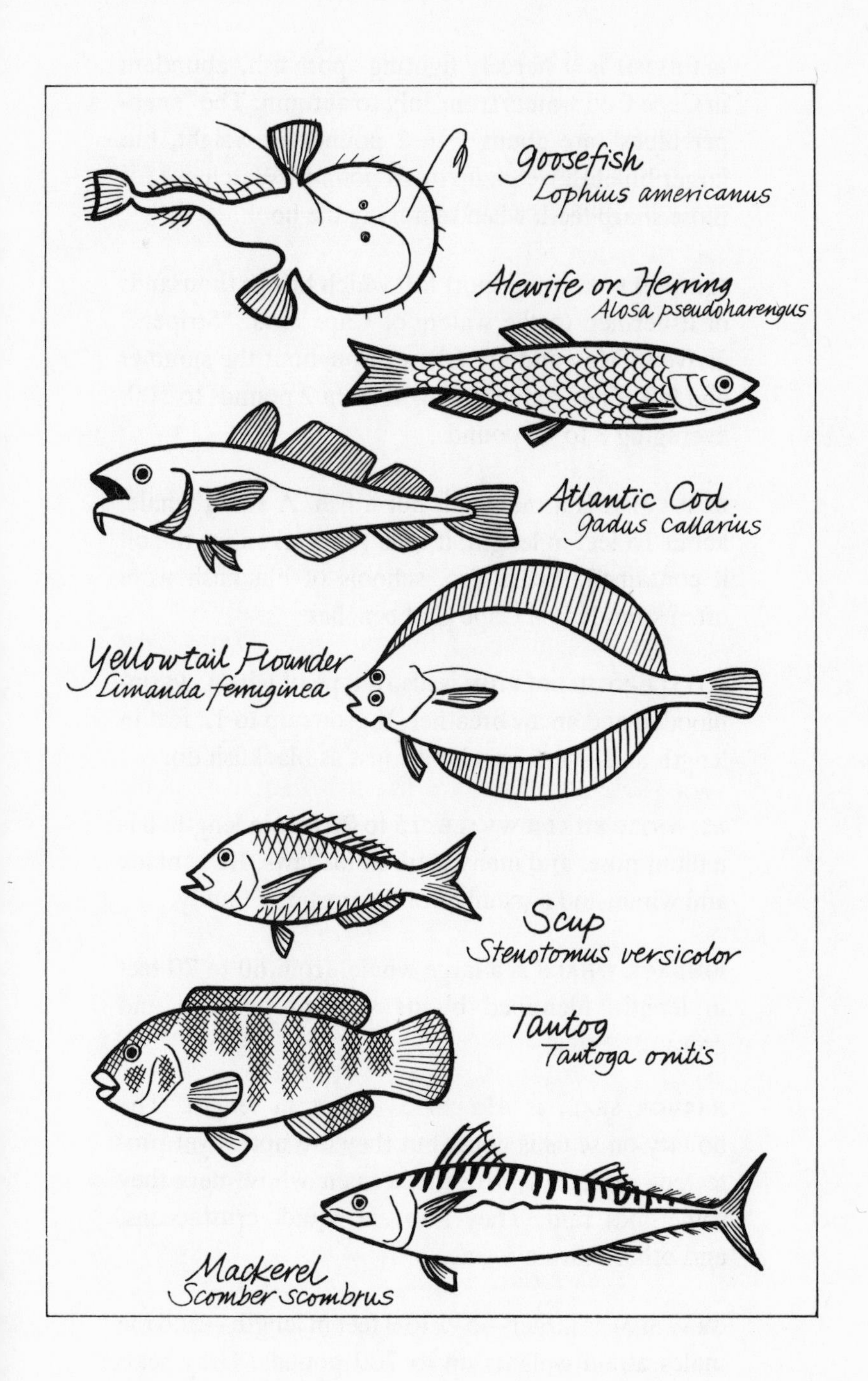
Goosefish
Lophius americanus
Alewife or Herring
Alosa pseudoharengus
Atlantic Cod
Gadus callarius
Yellowtail Flounder
Limanda ferruginea
Scup
Stenotomus versicolor
Tautog
Tautoga onitis
Mackerel
Scomber scombrus

BLUEFISH is a fiercely fighting sport fish, abundant in Cape Cod waters from July to autumn. The "snapper blues" are about 1 to 2 pounds in weight, but larger bluefish weigh up to 10 pounds. Watch out for those sharp teeth when removing the hook!

STRIPED BASS is the sport fish which brings thousands of fishermen to the waters of Cape Cod. "Stripers" arrive in May and are taken throughout the summer and fall. They range in weight from 2 pounds to 100, averaging 3 to 45 pounds.

BLACKFISH is a mammal, not a fish. A small whale, about 15 feet in length, it used to be taken for the oil it contained. Years ago, schools of blackfish were often stranded on Cape Cod beaches.

BOTTLE-NOSE DOLPHIN is also a type of whale, warm-blooded and an air breather. It grows up to 12 feet in length and swims in schools, just as blackfish do.

ATLANTIC KILLER WHALE, 15 to 20 feet in length, has a blunt nose, and many teeth in his jaws. He is black and white, and a member of the porpoise family.

FINBACK WHALE is a large whale, from 60 to 70 feet in length, identified by its slim proportions and grooved throat.

HARBOR SEAL, is 4½ to 5¼ feet in length. The bounty on seals is gone, but they are not as yet protected—especially from fishermen whose nets they sometimes raid. They also eat squid, crustaceans, and other marine forms.

GRAY SEAL is larger—5½ to 9 feet in length—and the males attain weights up to 700 pounds. Gray seals have long snouts and are known also as "horseheads."

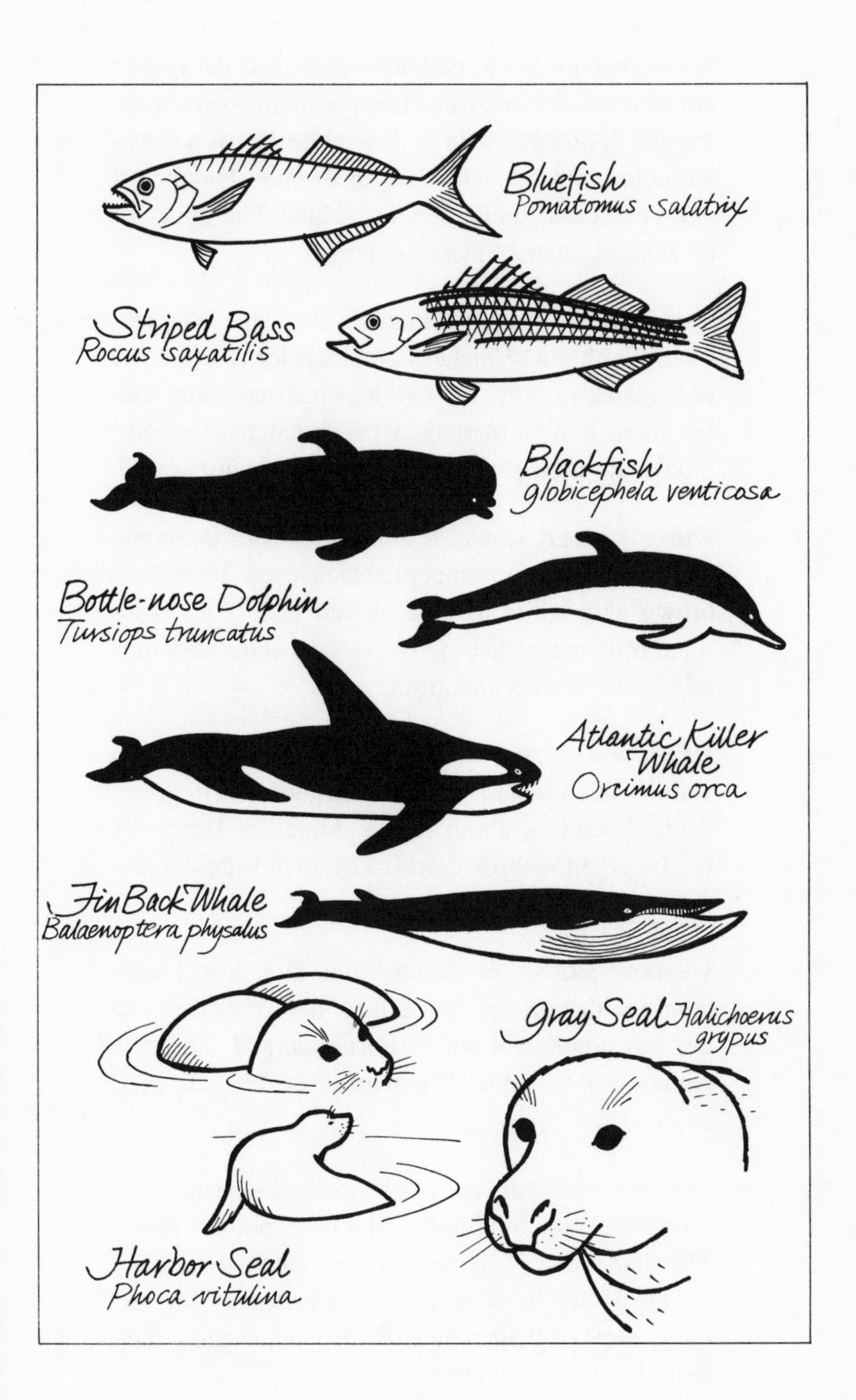
Bluefish
Pomatomus salatrix
Striped Bass
Roccus saxatilis
Blackfish
globicephela venticosa
Bottle-nose Dolphin
Tursiops truncatus
Atlantic Killer Whale
Orcimus orca
FinBack Whale
Balaenoptera physalus
Gray Seal Halichoerus grypus
Harbor Seal
Phoca vitulina

WHITE-TAILED DEER, or Virginia deer, is the largest land animal of Cape Cod. There is no mistaking one, feeding in an open field at dusk. The deer is a chestnut color with a black band on its chin. His throat, underparts and under legs are white. The antler of the male is 20 to 24 inches in length.

COTTONTAIL RABBIT abounds on the Cape. The cottontail is about 17 inches long; its color is a mixture of brown and gray, with white underparts and tail. Its home is a burrow in a berry patch or woods, though any clump of brush seems to serve just as well.

WHITE-FOOTED MOUSE is almost 7 inches in length, with very large, prominent, black eyes. Its coat is brown with white undersides and feet. This handsome little mouse lives in the woods, and, like squirrels, feeds on nuts and grain.

MEADOW JUMPING MOUSE is almost 9 inches long and not often seen. He lives in meadows or in grassy fields, bounding about like a miniature kangaroo. His fur is yellow-brown, with a white or yellowish underside, and he has an extra long tail.

MEADOW MOUSE, OR FIELD VOLE, is a dark brown mouse with gray fur beneath. It is 6½ inches long and has a compact body, short ears, and short tail. Numbers of field mice live in marshes. They are good swimmers.

EASTERN MOLES are about 6½ inches long with large forepaws, small hind feet, and a long, pointed snout. The Star-nosed Mole has a naked snout resembling a star. Moles have gray or brownish-gray fur and spend most of their time underground, digging their food: worms and insects.

White-tailed Deer
Odocoileus virginianus
Cottontail Rabbit
Sylvilagus floridanus
White-Footed Mouse
Peromyscus leucopus
Meadow Jumping Mouse
Zapus hudsonius hudsonius
Meadow Mouse or
Field Vole
Microtus pennsylvanicus
Eastern Mole
Scalopus aquaticus

MUSKRAT is about 2 feet in length, with a thickset body, short legs, and a thick wooly coat of dark brown fur. A cousin of the beaver, the muskrat spends much of its time in the water and constructs lodges of sod and mud for protection against winter's icy blasts.

WOODCHUCK, or groundhog, is about 2 feet in length, with a yellowish or rusty gray coat, a short bushy tail, and black feet. This animal hibernates in a deep burrow, coming up, it's said, on February 2nd—Groundhog Day—to prophesy the extent of winter by seeing, or not seeing, its shadow. This is not true, however, of Cape Cod woodchucks, which sleep the winter through.

NORTHEASTERN CHIPMUNK, about 9½ inches long, has a brown head and a gray and chestnut body with white and black stripes on the back. He loves to sit in the sun as a change from his underground home, which consists of an elaborate system of tunnels, and private rooms for all the family. He carries food to this storehouse in his large cheek pouches. Food is mostly nuts, seeds, berries, and an occasional garden vegetable.

MINK is 21 inches long, dark brown—nearly black—in color, with a spot of white on the chin and sometimes on the belly or chest. The mink is a hunter of wildfowl and small animals. He works by night and day, in and out of the water, and is so speedy that he is difficult to see.

LONG-TAILED WEASEL is a remarkably ferocious hunter. He sometimes kills for the sport alone. About 15 inches in length, he is reddish-brown, with white underparts. The end of his long tail is black.

Muskrat
Ondata zibethica
Northeastern Chipmunk
Tomias striatus
Woodchuck
Marmota monax
Long-tailed Weasel
Mustela frenata
Mink
Mustela vison

SKUNK is about 24 inches long and has long black fur except for a white patch on the neck and white stripes down the back. The skunk's defense against its enemies is well known. Skunks live in deep burrows, coming out to feed on grasshoppers and other insects, birds' eggs, young mice, and kitchen garbage.

RACCOON is about 32 inches in length. He is one of the large mammals with coarse, thick, gray fur, a black mask, and a ringed, bushy tail. He lives in burrows or hollow trees, coming out at night to feed on insects, frogs, fish, eggs, and corn.

GRAY SQUIRREL is 18 inches in length and has gray fur, white undersides, and a bushy tail. Those who feed wild birds know this persistent and wily creature who can make child's play out of the most complicated feeding stations. Gray Squirrels make nests of leaves in the forks and hollows of trees and lay away a store of nuts and berries for the winter.

RED SQUIRREL, 12 inches in length, is a noisy little rodent with chestnut fur. He has a white underside and large, prominent eyes. The Red Squirrel hoards a winter supply of food but also steals from the Gray Squirrel's storehouse. He lives in hollow logs or high in the trees and feeds on nuts and stolen eggs.

SOUTHERN FLYING SQUIRREL is about 9 inches in length with russet fur and white undersides. This squirrel sleeps by day and goes forth at night. It feeds on nuts and insects.

NORTHEASTERN RIVER OTTER, about 4 feet in length, is a nomad. He visits here in winter and travels through ponds, streams, and rivers, feeding on fish, small mammals, and frogs. A very playful relative of the weasel, the otter has small ears, webbed feet, and a broad snout.

Skunk
Mephitis mephitis
Raccoon
Procyon lotor
Red Squirrel
Tamiasclurus hudsonicus
Gray Squirrel
Sciurus carolinensis
Southern Flying Squirrel
Glaucomys volans
Northeastern River Otter
Lutra canadensis

MONARCH BUTTERFLY, orange and black, is very common. Its identifying marks are the black spots on the third vein of the hind wings of the male. Birds will not eat these butterflies because of their foul taste.

ANTS are social insects and live in communities. They are industrious and thrifty and work at jobs according to their class. They are identified by their narrow waists. Carpenter Ants are black, larger, ½ inch in length, and live in damp, dead wood.

BUMBLE BEES are easily noticed because of their large, fat, wooly bodies, an inch in length and striped yellow and black. They make their nests underground. The worker bumble bee stings severely.

HONEY BEES were imported from Europe to this country. For centuries, these little bees have been used to produce honey and pollinate fruit. They are also striped, orange and black.

WASPS and HORNETS have narrow waists and no fur. The White-Faced Hornet chews up wood and makes a paste of the pulp, fashioning it into a hanging nest. These often may be seen under the eaves of houses. Caution, these insects sting!

BLACK FIELD CRICKETS "chirp" by rubbing their forewings together. They are black, have long antennae, and are slightly less than an inch in length.

EARWIGS, about ⅝ inch in length, have very short wings and large tail pincers or forceps. They usually come out at night, preferring to spend the day in damp, dark places.

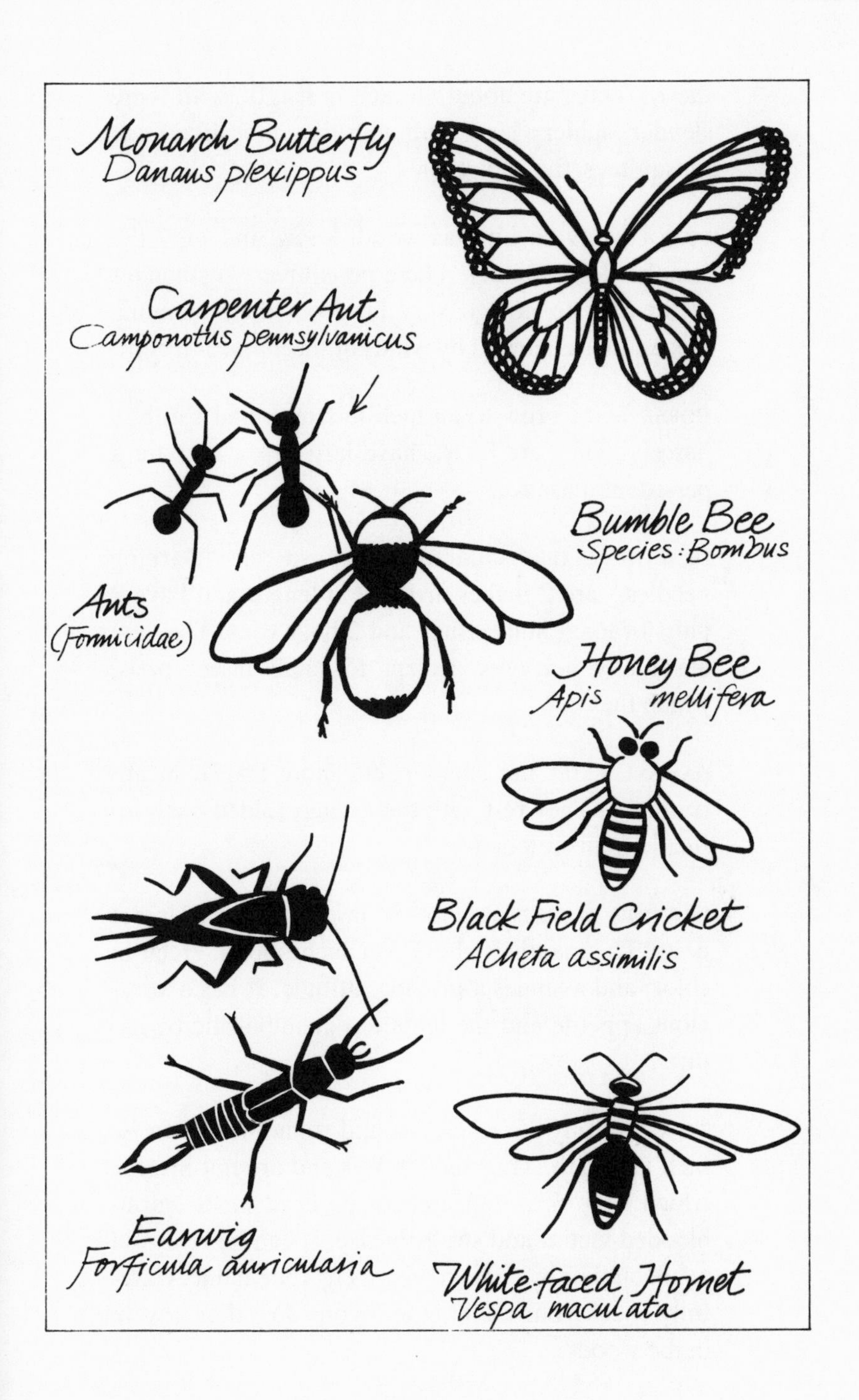
Monarch Butterfly
Danaus plexippus
Carpenter Ant
Camponotus pennsylvanicus
Bumble Bee
Species: Bombus
Ants
(Formicidae)
Honey Bee
Apis mellifera
Black Field Cricket
Acheta assimilis
Earwig
Forficula auricularia
White-faced Hornet
Vespa maculata

CRANE FLIES are about an inch in length, with long, slender, spidery legs. Although they look like huge mosquitoes, they don't bite.

MOSQUITOES do bite, as we all know, but only the females do the biting. These pests breed in stagnant water and do not go very far from their breeding places, unless carried by winds or mechanical means.

HORSE FLIES grow to an inch in length and can bite fiercely! They are black, have large eyes, and are a persistent nuisance.

DRAGON FLIES, commonly known as "Darning needles," are 2 inches or more in length and have 2 pairs of long, filmy wings and 2 huge eyes. They are absolutely harmless, except to small insect pests, which they eat.

DAMSEL FLIES are smaller and more fragile in appearance. They rest with their wings folded back instead of outstretched.

PRAYING MANTIS is another insect that eats insect pests. The mantis is about 3½ inches long, green in color, and assumes a praying attitude. It has a voracious appetite and the female is cannibalistic by nature.

TICKS are tiny parasites, flat and round, less than ¼ inch in length. They have 8 legs and are not insects, which have 6. A tick imbeds its head in its warm-blooded victim and swells in size. It can be removed by alcohol or by contact with a cigarette flame. Carefully check your clothing and your dog after a walk in the woods.

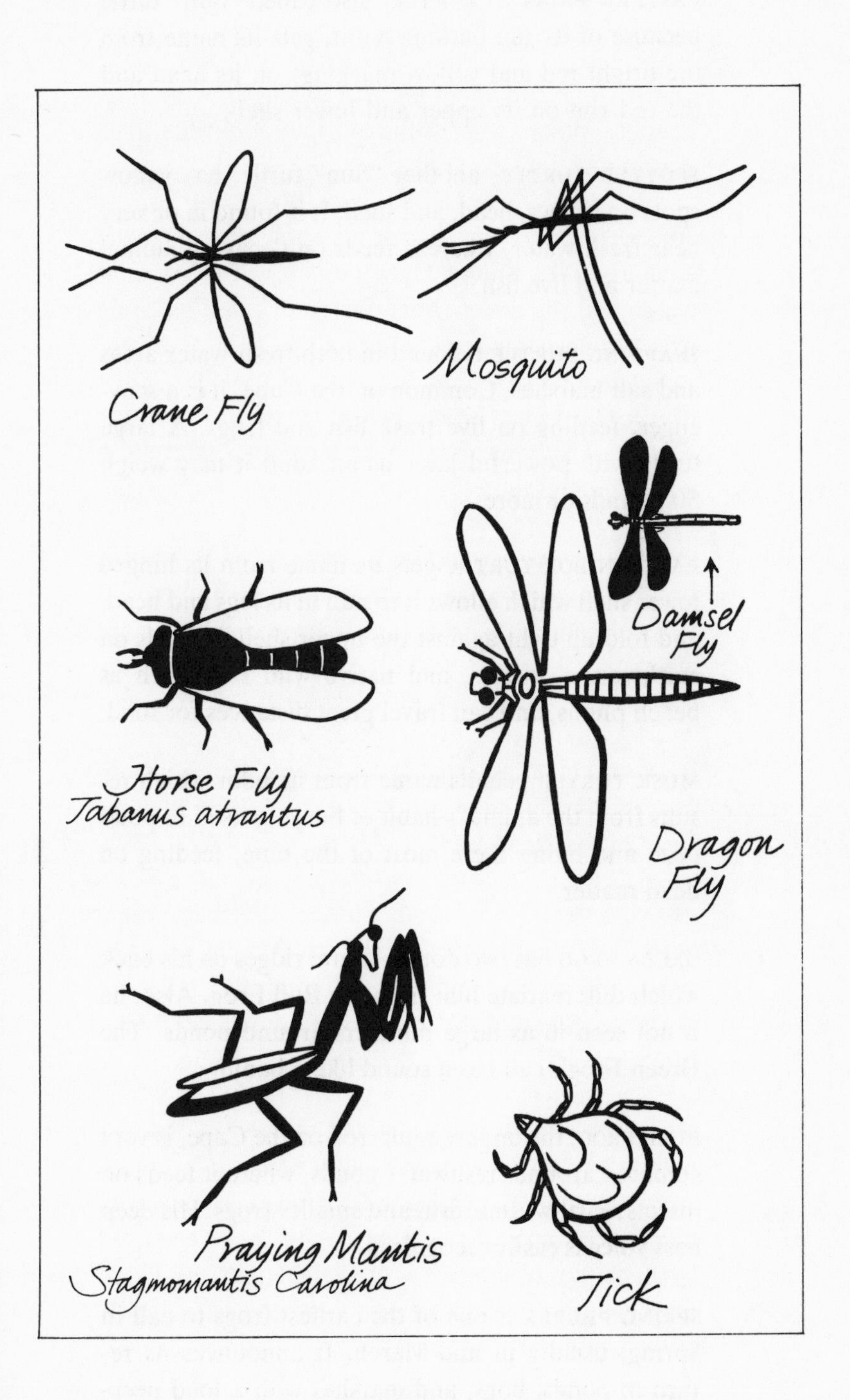
Crane Fly
Mosquito
Damsel Fly
Horse Fly
Tabanus atrantus
Dragon Fly
Praying Mantis
Stagmomantis Carolina
Tick

EASTERN PAINTED TURTLE, also called "Sun" turtle because of its sun-bathing habit, gets its name from the bright red and yellow markings on its head and the red rim on its upper and lower shell.

SPOTTED TURTLE, another "Sun" turtle, has yellow spots on its legs, head, and shell. It is found in or very near fresh water, where it feeds on decaying animal matter and live fish.

SNAPPING TURTLE is found in both fresh-water areas and salt marshes. Common on the Cape, it is a scavenger, feeding on live trash fish and frogs. A large turtle with powerful jaws, as an adult it may weigh 50 pounds or more.

EASTERN BOX TURTLE gets its name from its hinged lower shell which allows it to pull in its legs and head, and fold up tight against the upper shell. It feeds on earthworms, insects, and native wild fruit such as beach plums, and can travel great distances for food.

MUSK TURTLE gets its name from its odor which results from the animal's habit of burying itself in pond ooze and living there most of the time, feeding on dead matter.

GREEN FROG has two dorsal-lateral ridges on his back which differentiate him from the Bull Frog. Also, he is not seen in as large numbers around ponds. The Green Frog's call has a sound like a banjo.

BULL FROG, the largest adult frog on the Cape, is very common around freshwater ponds, where it feeds on insects, earthworms, fish, and smaller frogs. His deep bass voice is easily recognized.

SPRING PEEPER is one of the earliest frogs to call in Spring, usually in mid-March. It announces its return to ponds, bogs, and marshes with a loud peeping sound. The average adult is about 1 inch long.

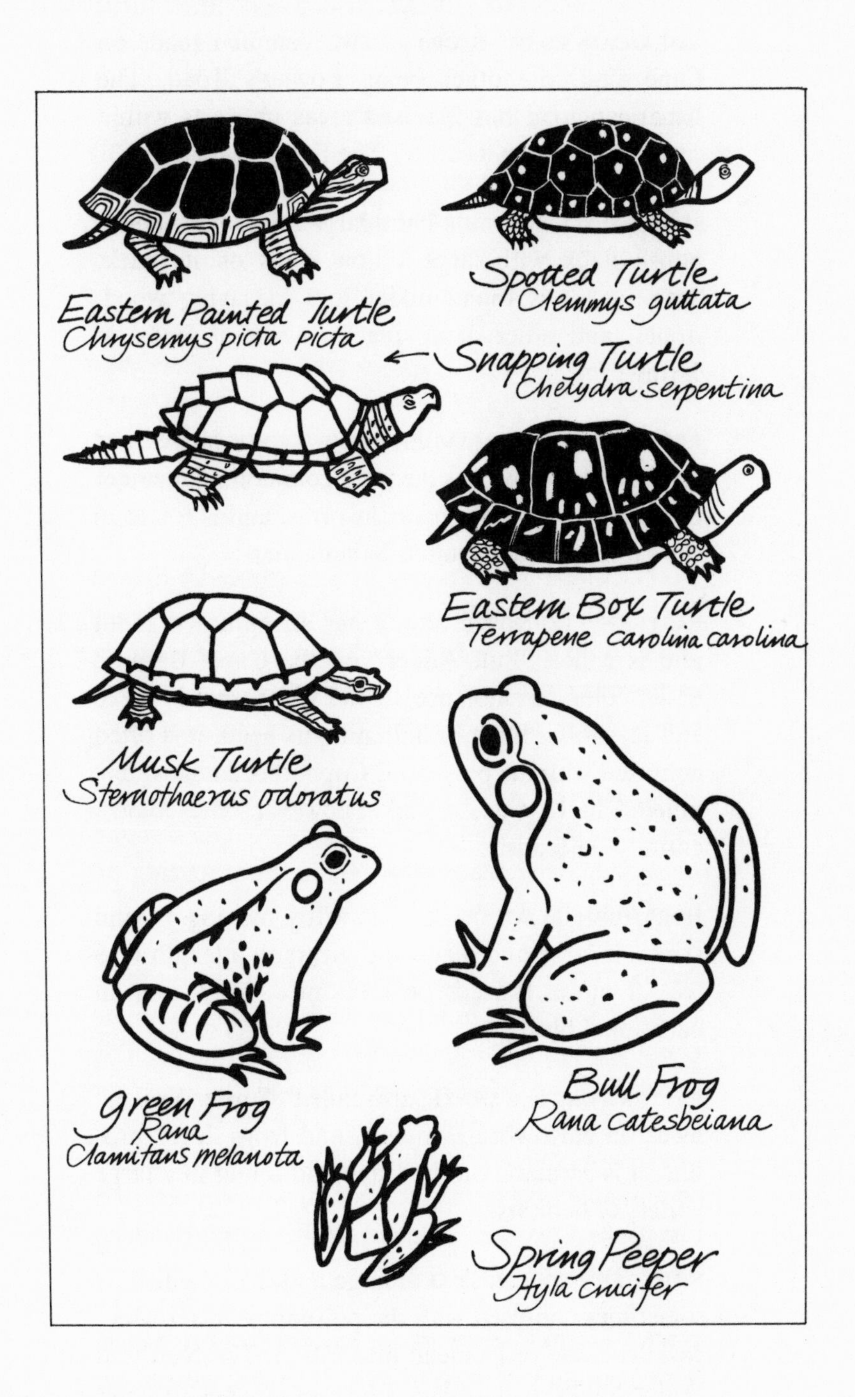
Spotted Turtle
Clemmys guttata
Eastern Painted Turtle
Chrysemys picta picta
Snapping Turtle
Chelydra serpentina
Eastern Box Turtle
Terrapene carolina carolina
Musk Turtle
Sternothaerus odoratus
Bull Frog
Rana catesbeiana
Green Frog
Rana
Clamitans melanota
Spring Peeper
Hyla crucifer

AMERICAN TOAD is one of two common toads on Cape Cod, the other being Fowler's Toad. The American toad has 2 raised areas or warts within each dark spot on its body. The Fowler's toad has 3.

SPOTTED SALAMANDER has a large round head and is bluish-black with large yellow spots on its back. Secretive, it is found under logs, decaying wood, stones, and other damp places, where it feeds on earthworms.

RED-BACKED SALAMANDER has two color phases, red and blackish gray. It is the most common salamander on Cape Cod, feeds on earthworms, and is found in the same areas as Spotted Salamanders.

EASTERN HOG-NOSED SNAKE has an upturned snout and is called "Puff Adder" on the Cape. Because of its color resemblance to the Copperhead Snake and its similar habit of flattening its head, it is often confused with the poisonous Copperhead and widely killed. The Hog-nosed snake, however, feeds almost entirely on toads.

NORTHERN BLACK RACER, a swiftly moving ground snake, is large and black and grows to a length of 6 feet or more. It feeds on rats, mice, frogs, and an occasional bird.

EASTERN GARTER SNAKE, also called "Garden Snake," feeds on earthworms, insects, and frogs. Very prolific, it is common on the Cape and found in a large variety of habitats.

NORTHERN WATER SNAKE, large and thick-bodied, is sometimes confused with the poisonous Water-Moccasin because of its mean disposition. The Northern Water Snake is harmless, however, except to frogs and fish which, like itself, live in freshwater areas.

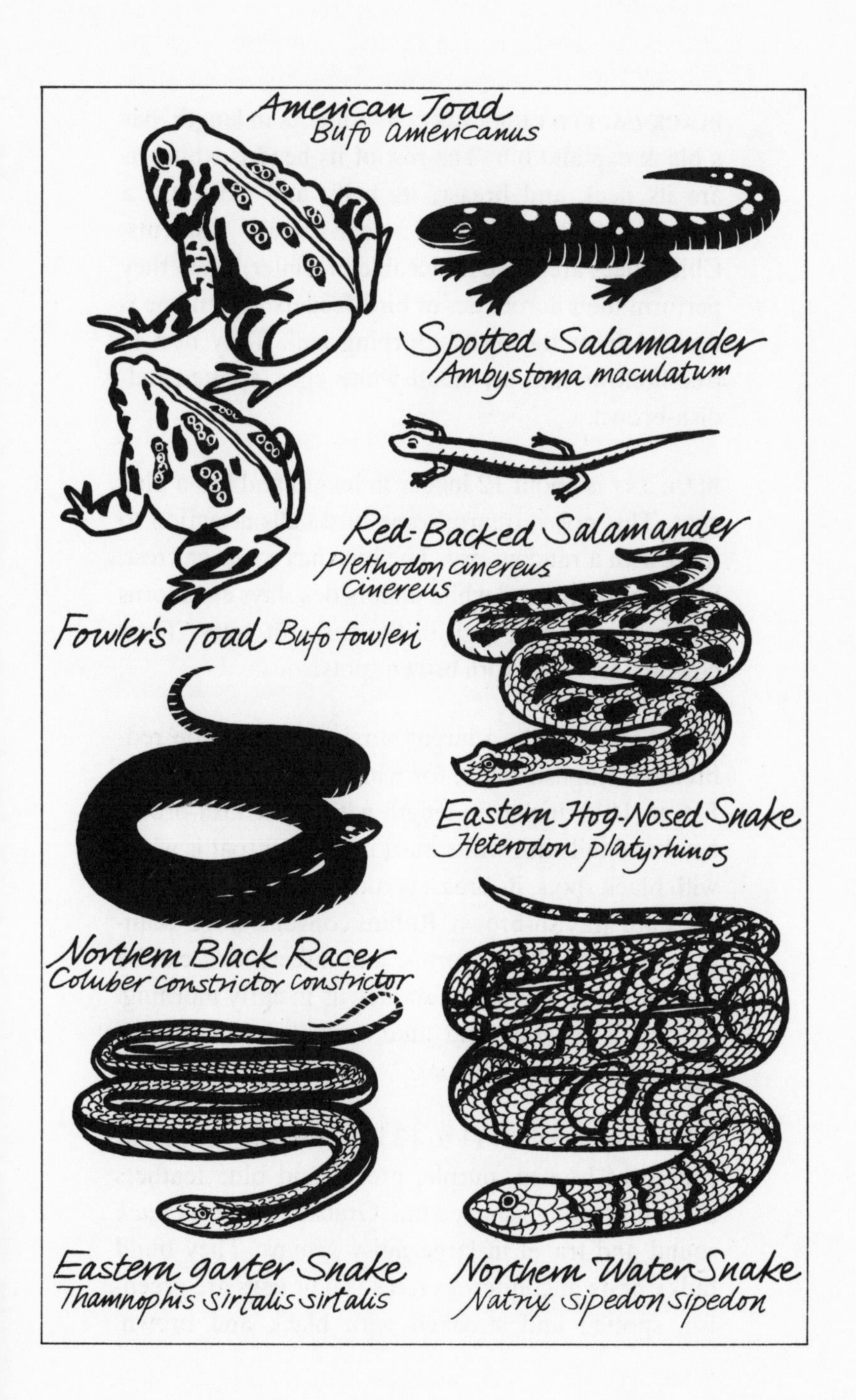
American Toad
Bufo americanus
Spotted Salamander
Ambystoma maculatum
Red-Backed Salamander
Plethodon cinereus cinereus
Fowler's Toad Bufo fowleri
Eastern Hog-Nosed Snake
Heterodon platyrhinos
Northern Black Racer
Coluber constrictor constrictor
Eastern garter Snake
Thamnophis sirtalis sirtalis
Northern Water Snake
Natrix sipedon sipedon

BLACK-CAPPED CHICKADEE, 5¼ inches in length, has a black cap and bib. The rest of its head is white, as are its neck and breast; its belly and sides are a creamy yellow. Cheerful year-round residents, Chickadees are more noticeable in winter, when they perform their acrobatics at bird-feeders. The name is derived from the birds' chirping call. They nest in tree hollows and lay small white eggs, spotted reddish-brown.

BLUE JAY is about 12 inches in length and has a blue coat. This noisy, quarrelsome bird calls attention to itself with a raucous cry. The bird has a cap or crest, black markings and white undersides. Jays eat acorns and nuts and nest high in the forks of trees. Their eggs are greenish, with brown spots.

ROBIN is a thrush, a larger version of the little red-breasted English robin, for which it was named. It is 8½ to 10½ inches in length with a blackish-brown head and tail with white markings. Its throat is white with black spots, its breast is ruddy, and its wings and back are grayish-brown. Robins consume huge quantities of caterpillars, worms, and insects, and can be seen hopping over fields and lawns in early morning. Its nest is of grass and mud, and its greenish-blue eggs are about an inch long.

PURPLE GRACKLE is 11 to 13 inches in length and has iridescent bronze, purple, green, and blue feathers and a long wedge-shaped tail. Grackles make a *chuck* sound and travel in large noisy groups. They build bulky nests in coniferous trees. Their eggs are greenish, spotted and streaked with black and brown.

Black-Capped Chickadee
Parus atricapillus
Blue Jay
Cyanocitta cristata
Robin
Turdus migratorius
Purple grackle
Quiscalus quiscala

CATBIRD, about 9 inches long, is dark gray in color except for the tail and the top of the head, which are black. Its nest, made of twigs and grape-vine bark, is found in bushes or vines. The eggs are dark glossy greenish-blue. The bird's call is like a cat cry, and it also imitates the calls of other birds. It eats insect pests and cultivated fruit crops.

SLATE-COLORED JUNCO, 6¼ inches in length, is gray-colored with white lower breast and belly and outer tail feathers. This is another bird which nests and feeds on the ground. Its eggs are white, spotted with brown. The Junco spends the winter on Cape Cod and its diet is mainly weed seeds.

SONG SPARROW, 6½ inches long, has a large brown spot in the center of the breast and long, rounded tail. The top of the head is reddish-brown, mottled with blackish streaks. It has a light gray streak over the eye, a dark line through the eye and two on the lower jaw. Breast and sides are white, streaked with brown. It nests on the ground or in a bush and its eggs are whitish and speckled with brown. This bird, famous for its sweet song, eats harmful insects and the seeds of weeds.

TOWHEE, 7 ½ to 8¾ inches long, has a black head, neck, wings and tail, the latter two with white markings (male). Females are brown instead of black. It has reddish sides, and its breast and belly are white. These "Ground Robins" usually have a sunken nest —often roofed over. Their eggs are white, and finely spotted with brown. They feed on insect pests and their name comes from their call, tow/-hee, tow/-hee.

Catbird
Dumetella carolinensis
Slate-Colored Junco
Junco hyemalis
Song Sparrow
Melospiza melodia
Towhee
Pipilo erythropthalmus

ORIOLE is about 8 inches in length. The male Baltimore Oriole is bright orange, with black head, wing, and tail markings. The female is olive and yellow in color. Their call is a full-throated chirp. They build hanging nests of grass and string, and their eggs are white with streaks and patches of brown and black. They live here from May to September.

RED-WINGED BLACKBIRD, 7½ to 9½ inches long, has a jet black body and wings and bright red shoulder patches with buff edges. The female is smaller, gray-brown in color, and streaked with black. She does not have the distinctive patches. The birds nest in grass or bushes, and their eggs are pale blue with dark spots and streaks. They eat the caterpillars of the gypsy moth, and other troublesome insects.

BARN SWALLOW, 6 to 7 inches long, has a deeply forked tail, dark blue color, buff undersides, and a chestnut forehead, throat, and upper breast. These swallows build nests of mud, straw and feathers attached to the rafters of barns and sheds. The eggs are white with brown spots. Barn swallows feed on injurious insects and moths.

GOLDFINCH or Wild Canary is 5 to 5½ inches in length. The male is bright canary-yellow with a black cap, wings, and tail. The female is dull olive-yellow with wings and tail much like the male. The Goldfinch builds a cup-like nest of grass and moss, lined with down; its eggs are bluish-white. It flies in graceful, undulating glides. The male has a sweet and canary-like song.

Baltimore Oriole
Icterus galbula
Red-Winged Blackbird
Agelaius phoeniceus
Barn Swallow
Hirundo rustica
Goldfinch
Spinus tristus

WHIP-POOR-WILL, about 10 inches long, is a songbird of the night. With its enormous, bristle-surrounded mouth, it eats moths and other insects. It is mottled and barred, black, brown, and gray in color, with a thin band under the throat that is white in the male and buff in the female. It builds no nest, leaving its creamy white eggs, speckled with purple, in a bed of leaves on the ground. Often heard, but rarely seen, it is recognized by its call, whip′-poor-will′.

WHITE-BREASTED NUTHATCH is 5 to 6 inches long. Its upper parts are light blue-gray with black markings, its wings marked black and white. It has white underparts and sides of head and a black cap. The Nut Hatch makes its nest in a tree or hollow post, and lays eggs much like the chickadee's—white, speckled with brown—but larger. It spends much of its time upside down and is able to walk *down* a tree. Its diet is mostly insects.

DOWNY WOODPECKER, 6½ to 7 inches long, is spotted and checkered black and white with a white back. The male has a small scarlet patch on the back of its head. The bird nests in a hollow tree or stump; its eggs are white. This is the smallest woodpecker and the most useful, because of its diet of wood-boring insects and caterpillars. The HAIRY WOODPECKER, less common, has identical markings and a longer bill, but is 8½ to 10½ inches in length.

FLICKER, about 12 inches long, is the most common migratory woodpecker of Cape Cod. It is brown, with a scarlet crescent on its neck. Shafts and linings of both wings are yellow; black dots and crescent on breast; black patches below eyes (males only); black bars on wings and back; gray top and back of head.

Whip-Poor-Will
Caprimulgus vociferus
White-Breasted
Nuthatch
Sitta carolinensis
Downy Woodpecker
Dendrocopus pubescens
Flicker
Colaptes auratus

SCREECH OWL, about 8 to 10 inches long, has distinguishing ear tufts and large yellow eyes. Screech Owls have 2 color phases: gray and reddish-brown. Its diet is mainly mice, moths, caterpillars, beetles, and an occasional small bird. Its mournful, wailing cry is heard at night.

GREAT HORNED OWL, 20 to 23 inches in length, has very few natural enemies. A nocturnal bird, it is also found during the day. The tufts of feathers on its head give the bird its name. Its diet consists of small mammals, snakes, frogs, birds, and grasshoppers.

SAW-WHET OWL averages about 7 inches in size, and has a very large head in proportion to its body. It usually lives in deep forest and is so tame that it allows concerned people, who assume it is injured, to pick it up when it ventures out in winter to roads and open areas. It feeds mainly on mice.

BOB-WHITE OF QUAIL is 10 inches long. The male has reddish-brown upper parts, a white line over each eye, and a white throat patch, bordered with black. His short tail is gray, and his upper breast, neck, and sides are brownish red; breast and belly are whitish. The female is paler, without the black on the head and with buff markings instead of white. The birds nest on the ground in bushes and grass; the eggs are white. Quail feed mainly on destructive garden pests and weed seeds.

MYRTLE WARBLER is a year-'round resident of Cape Cod. It is a small bird, about 5 inches in length, with a yellow crown and shoulder patches and a yellow rump patch. Myrtle Warbler feeds on berries, particularly bayberries, and insects.

Great Horned Owl
Bubo virginianus
Screech Owl
Otus asio
Saw-Whet Owl
Aegolius acadicus
Bobwhite or Quail
Colinus virginianus
Myrtle
Warbler
Dendroica coronata

GREAT BLUE HERON feeds on fish, small mammals, small reptiles and amphibians. It is often seen in tidal marshes and along freshwater ponds. It will stand motionless in water, wait for prey to come into reach, and then shoot out its rapier-like bill at its victim. A very large bird, standing almost 4 feet in height, the heron has a crested head with long plumes. Its flight is graceful.

RED-TAILED HAWK, 19 to 25 inches in height, is a soaring hawk, feeding mainly on small mammals and snakes. It is the common large hawk of Cape Cod. In bright sunlight, look for the glint of red on the tail that sets it apart from other large hawks.

SPARROW HAWK, 9 to 12 inches in length, and very common on the Cape, is a small falcon. It seems to stand still in air, with fluttering wings, while hunting its food—insects and small mammals.

GREAT BLACK-BACKED GULL, about 30 inches in length, is the largest gull on Cape Cod and is increasing in numbers. It is white with a black mantle, and with its wings folded over its back it looks as if it has a black back.

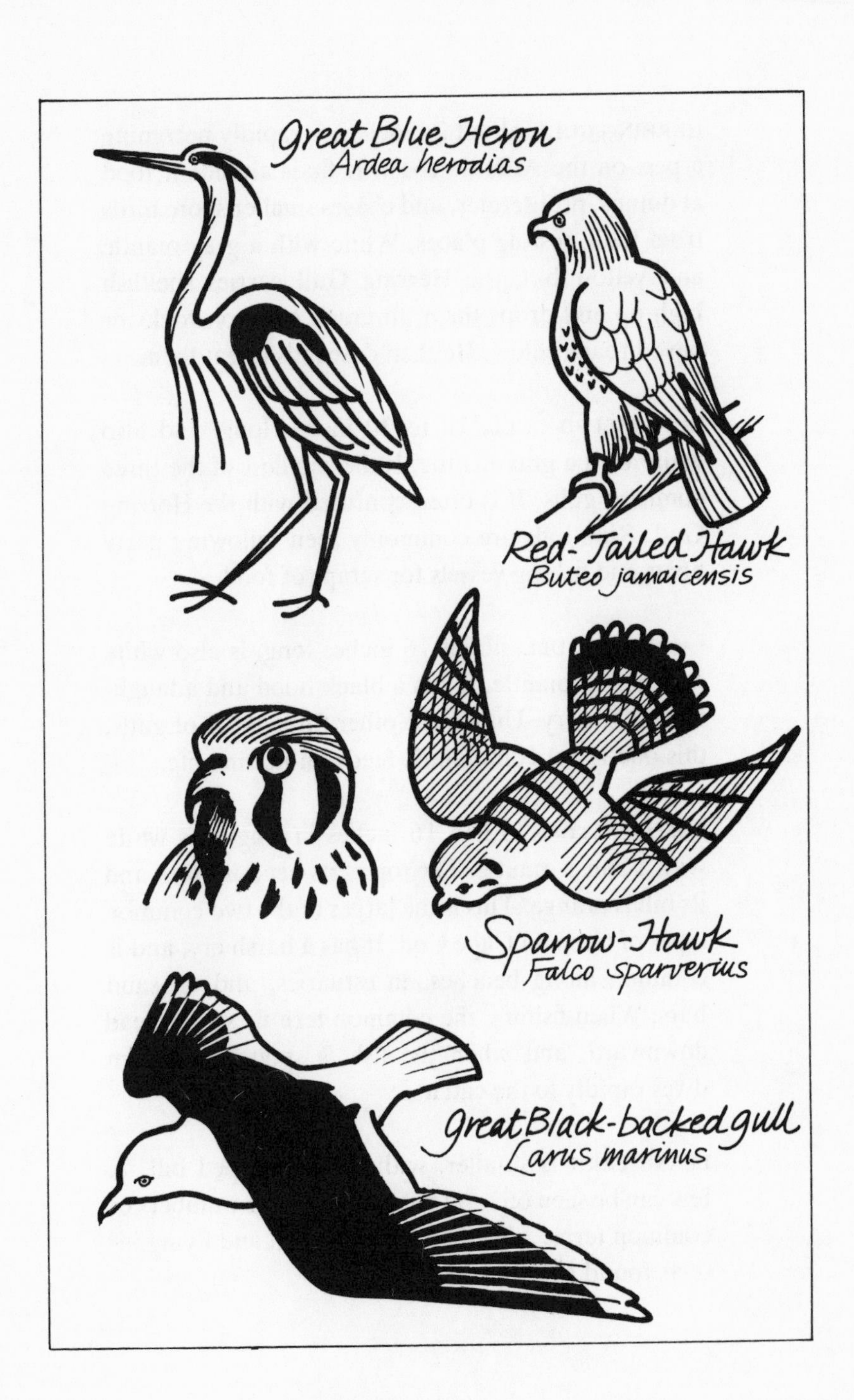
Great Blue Heron
Ardea herodias
Red-Tailed Hawk
Buteo jamaicensis
Sparrow-Hawk
Falco sparverius
Great Black-backed gull
Larus marinus

HERRING GULL, about 24 inches, is rapidly becoming a pest on the Atlantic coast. It finds abundant food at dumps, proliferates, and chases smaller shore birds from their nesting places. White with a gray mantle and yellow bill, the Herring Gull carries shellfish high up and drops them, to crack open on rocks or paved roads below. He then descends to eat them.

RING-BILLED GULL, 18 to 20 inches long, and also white with a gray mantle, is the smallest of the three common gulls. It is often confused with the Herring Gull. Ring-bills are commonly seen following party boats and fishing vessels for scraps of food.

LAUGHING GULL, about 16 inches long, is also white with a gray mantle. It has a black hood and a laugh-like call or cry. Unlike the other three types of gulls, this one is not common. It feeds on marine life.

COMMON TERN, 13 to 16 inches in length, is white with a bluish mantle. The top of its head is black and its bill is orange. This is the larger of the two common types of terns on Cape Cod. It has a harsh cry, and is common along beaches, in estuaries, and on sand bars. When fishing, the common tern flies with head downward, and when the fish is spotted, the tern dives rapidly to the catch.

LEAST TERN is smaller, with a black-tipped bill. A few can be seen on sand bars among large numbers of common terns. They feed on small fish and flying insects found near marshes.

Herring gull
Larus argentatus
Laughing gull
Larus
atricilla
Ring-Billed
gull
Larus delawarensis
Least Tern
Sterna albifrons
Common Tern
Sterna hirundo

OLD SQUAW male is up to 21 inches in size, the female up to 17. These sea ducks change their plumage twice yearly. The male body colors are chiefly blackish-brown, gray and white; the bill pink with black tip and base; feet pale gray. The adult females are not as conspicuously marked as the males and they do not have the long thin tail. They are excellent divers and swift in flight. They feed on marine animals.

COMMON EIDER, or Sea-duck, is 22 to 26 inches long and the Cape's largest sea duck. The males are distinctively marked with a black belly and a white back. The females are brown, barred with black. Note the long-nose profile. They were once slaughtered for their down, with which they line their nests and cover their eggs. They generally keep well out to sea and feed mostly on mussels.

SURF SCOTER is 18 to 21 inches long with a black body and 1 or 2 white head patches fore-and-aft on the male. The female is dusky-brown in color and may have light face patches.

AMERICAN SCOTER is 17 to 21 inches long. The adult male is overall black, including bill, which has a yellow-orange base. The female and young have a bill without a hump, and their plumage is grayish-brown. There are no white marks in either sex. This is an expert diving duck, commonly and mistakenly called a "coot." It feeds mostly on mussels.

WHITE-WINGED SCOTER is 20 to 23 inches long. The male has white wing patches, a small white eye patch and a swollen reddish-orange bill. The female is paler and brown, with two gray head patches. Strong fliers, they take off in a slow, clumsy way.

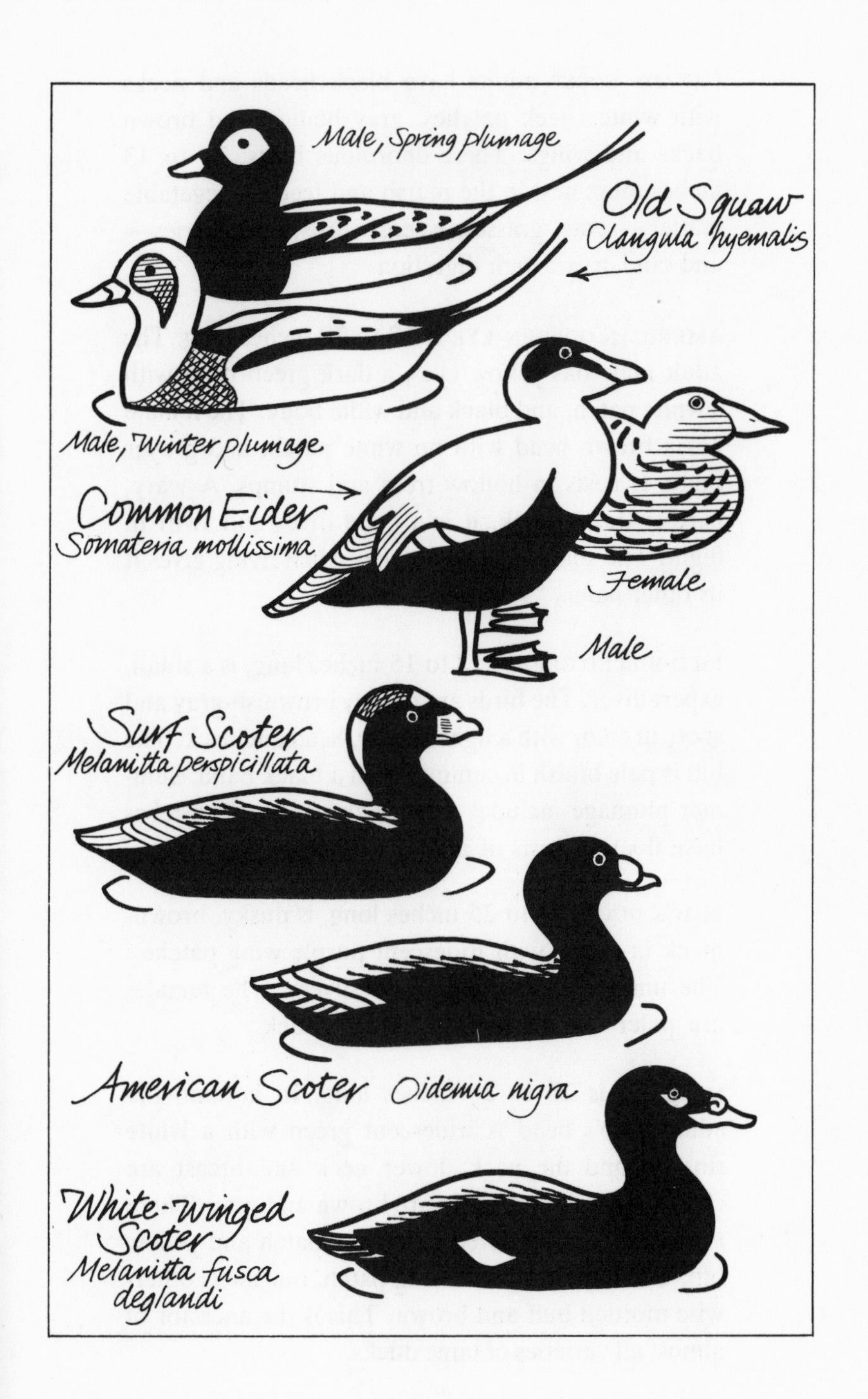
Male, Spring plumage
Old Squaw
Clangula hyemalis
Male, Winter plumage
Common Eider
Somateria mollissima
Female
Male
Surf Scoter
Melanitta perspicillata
American Scoter Oidemia nigra
White-winged Scoter
Melanitta fusca deglandi

CANADA GOOSE adults have black heads and necks with white cheek patches, gray bodies, and brown backs and wings. These enormous birds, 25 to 43 inches long, nest in the marsh and feed on vegetable matter—roots, grasses, weeds, seeds, and berries—and sand, to aid their digestion.

AMERICAN GOLDEN-EYE is 17 to 20 inches long. The adult male has yellow eyes, a dark green head with a white patch, and black and white body. The female has a brown head with no white patch, and grayer body. It nests in hollow trees and stumps. A wary, hard-to-decoy duck, it is a good diver and swift in flight. The sharp sound it makes when flying gives it its other name, "Whistler."

PIED-BILLED GREBE, 12 to 15 inches long, is a small, expert diver. The birds are mainly brownish-gray and sooty in color with a lighter belly, head and neck. The bill is pale bluish in summer with a black band. Summer plumage includes a black throat patch. Grebes have floating nests of muddy vegetation.

BLACK DUCK, 21 to 25 inches long, is dusky, brown-black in color, with iridescent purple wing patches. The undersides are white and silvery. The females are paler and more brown than black.

MALLARD is 20 to 28 inches long. In autumn the adult male's head is iridescent green with a white ring around the neck; lower neck and breast are chestnut; back and wings are brown and gray. There is also a white-bordered blue wing patch and yellow bill. The female has the wing patch, but she is otherwise mottled buff and brown. This is the ancestor of almost all varieties of tame ducks.

Canada Goose
Branta canadensis
American Golden-eye
Glaucionetta clangula
americana
Pied-
billed
grebe
Podilymbus
podiceps
Black Duck
Anas rubripes
Mallard
Anas platyrhynchos

AMERICAN WIDGEON or BALDPATE is 18 to 22 inches long. The male has a pale whitish head and neck, a white belly and white forewing patch, and a dark green patch through and behind the eye. The female lacks the green patch and bald pate, and is paler.

RED-BREASTED MERGANSER is 20 to 25 inches long. The adult male has a blackish-green head and crest, broad white collar, black and white body and wings; breast, bill, and feet are red. The female is smaller and has a white throat and reddish-brown head, a lighter back and a square white patch. The male's wing patch is divided. These birds are expert divers, feeding mainly on fish, which they snare with their saw-tooth bills. The Common Merganser or Shell-drake is larger by 3 inches. The male has a plain white breast and no crest. The female's head is brown.

BLUE-WINGED TEAL, 15 to 16 inches long, has blue and green wing patches separated by a white band. Its body is mottled brown and buff. The male's head is dusky gray with a white crescent.

GREEN-WINGED TEAL, 13½ to 15½ inches long, is a small and beautiful bird identified by its green lower wing patches. The male's head is chestnut, with a green patch and a black tuft at the back; there is also a white crescent before the wing.

BUFFLE-HEAD, 13 to 15 inches long, is a diver identified by its small body and large, puffy head. The adult male's head is dark purple-green with a white patch, the female's dusky brown. The male's body and wings are black and white, the female's brown and white. The female has her white patch back of the eye, and she also has a white wing patch.

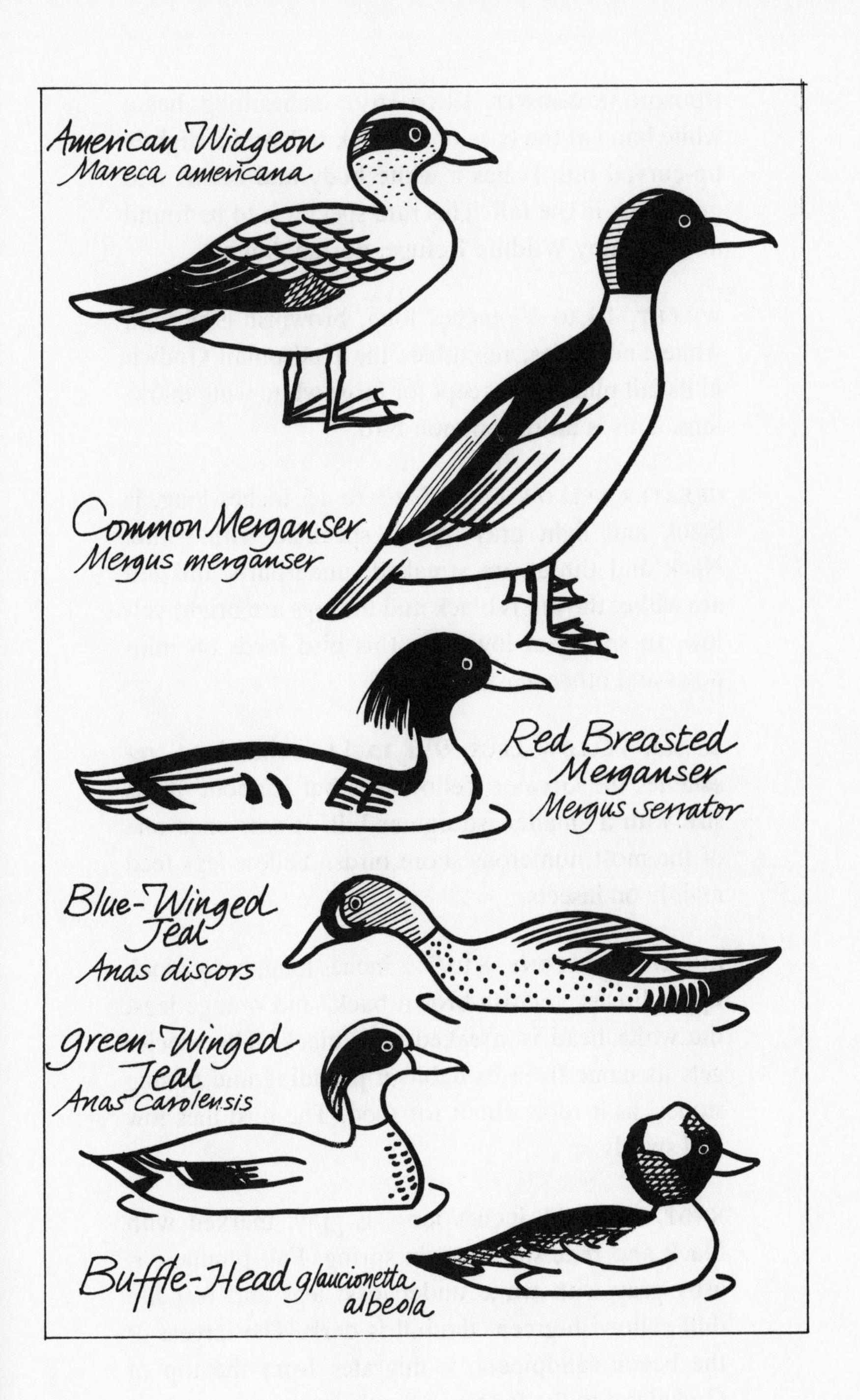
American Widgeon
Mareca americana
Common Merganser
Mergus merganser
Red Breasted
Merganser
Mergus serrator
Blue-Winged
Teal
Anas discors
green-Winged
Teal
Anas carolensis
Buffle-Head glaucionetta
albeola

HUDSONIAN GODWIT, 14 to 16½ inches long, has a white band at the base of its black tail, and a slightly up-curved bill. It has a white body and breast and gray back in the fall. This rare species is to be found at Monomoy Wildlife Refuge, during August.

WILLET, 14 to 17 inches long, brownish-gray with white undersides, resembles the Hudsonian Godwit in its fall plumage, except for large white wing markings. This is an uncommon bird.

GREATER YELLOW LEGS, 13½ to 15 inches long, is black and light gray above, speckled with white. Neck and throat are streaked, underparts and tail are white; the bill is black and the legs are bright yellow. In spring at low tides this bird feeds on minnows and other marine life.

LESSER YELLOW LEGS, 9½ to 11 inches long, resembles the Greater Yellow legs but is about ⅔ its size with a smaller, straighter bill. It was once one of the most numerous shore birds. Yellow legs feed mainly on insects.

RUDDY TURNSTONE, 8 to 9½ inches long, has a black upper breast, reddish-brown back, and orange legs; the white head is streaked with black. The species gets its name from its habit of prodding and raising stones as it roots about for food. The bird flies low and swiftly.

KNOT, 10 to 11 inches long, is gray, marked with black and reddish-brown in spring. Fall plumage is ashy gray with white undersides; legs and feet are dull yellowish-green, the bill is dark. The largest of the beach sandpipers, it migrates from the top of Greenland to the far tip of South America.

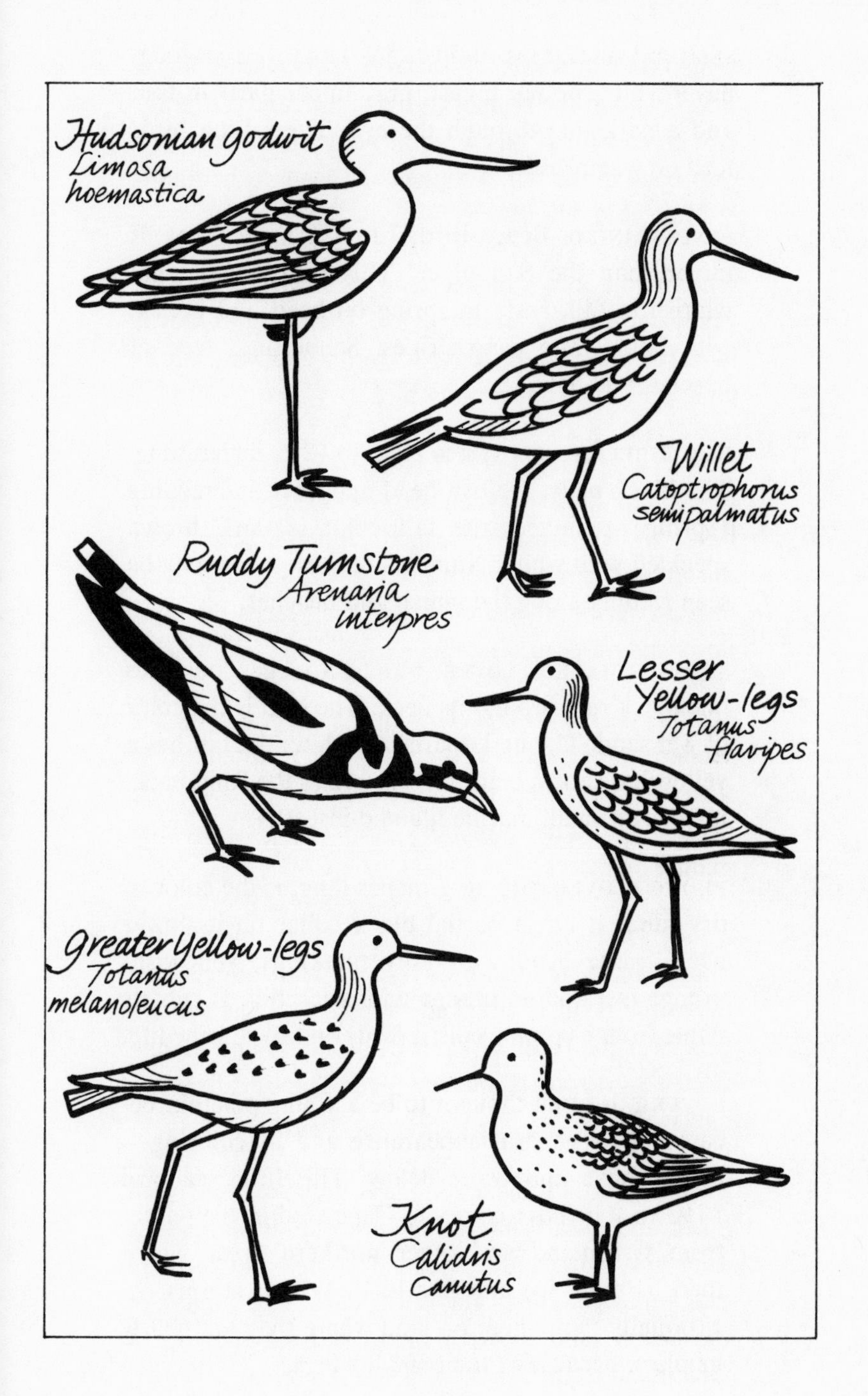
Hudsonian godwit
Limosa
hoemastica
Willet
Catoptrophorus
semipalmatus
Ruddy Turnstone
Arenaria
interpres
Lesser
Yellow-legs
Totanus
flavipes
Greater Yellow-legs
Totanus
melanoleucus
Knot
Calidris
canutus

SEMI-PALMATED SANDPIPER, 5½ to 6½ inches long, has a white spotted breast, gray upper parts in fall, and a dark line through the eye. These little birds feed on water insects.

SANDERLING or Beach Bird, 7 to 8½ inches long, is larger than the Sandpiper. This bird's colors are whitish in fall, rusty in spring on head and breast, with bold white wing stripes. Sanderlings feed at beaches and flats.

BLACK-BELLIED PLOVER is 10½ to 13½ inches long. The black belly, whitish head and back is breeding (spring) plumage; the fall color is dark brown speckled with white. Numbers of these birds may be seen feeding along the marsh and beaches.

SEMI-PALMATED PLOVER, 6½ to 8 inches long, has one black ring around its neck. The bird is the color of wet sand. The underparts are white; the bill has a yellow base and a black tip. Known as the Ring-neck, it feeds on small marine life and insects.

PIPING PLOVER, 6½ to 7 inches long, is the color of dry sand. It has a partial black collar on its lower neck, white head with ashy markings; yellowish-orange feet and an orange and black bill. It gets its name from its piping call; it feeds on tiny marine life.

DOVEKIE is often thought to be a young penguin because of its general appearance and its coloring—black above and white below. This little sea bird (7½ to 9 inches) comes to Cape Cod in the winter from Greenland and other northern areas where there is more ice and less food. Winter storms occasionally blow them on land where they are nearly helpless, because of their small wings.

Semipalmated Sandpiper
Ereunetes pusillus
Sanderling
Crocelina alba
Black-Bellied Plover
Squatarola Squatarola
Semipalmated Plover
Charadrius semipalmatus
Piping Plover
Charadrius melodus
Dovekie
Plautus alle

ABOUT THE AUTHOR

PAUL GIAMBARBA'S graphic designs have won awards and recognition in the United States and abroad. From 1955 to 1960 he worked and traveled extensively in Europe, settling on Cape Cod upon his return home, where he now lives with his wife and two children. He has been a weekly contributor to Scholastic Magazines periodicals for elementary school children for over ten years. In 1965, he began The Scrimshaw Press in an effort to make abundantly illustrated original material available in paperback form at modest prices.

INDEX